Fashion Dolls
EXCLUSIVELY
INTERNATIONAL

ID &
PRICE GUIDE
to World-Wide
Fashion Dolls

by
Robert Gardner

Photography by
Margo Rana

Published by

Hobby
House
Press

Hobby House Press, Inc.
Grantsville, Maryland 21536

DEDICATION

In remembrance of my parents Robert Gardner Senior and Marjorie S. Gardner; this book is dedicated to them for their love and encouragement throughout my entire life. They were always there for my sisters and me and they will be in our hearts forever.

ACKNOWLEDGMENTS

I would like to express my deepest gratitude to the following people for various reasons. First of all, thanks to Judy Schizas for her wonderful friendship all of these years and for sharing some of her own dolls for inclusion in this book. Judy really cares about all Barbie doll collectors and helps to persuade Mattel to produce the type of dolls that we collectors really want. I feel she is one of Mattel's greatest assets.

Many thanks to Alice Azpeitia for graciously thinking of me as I prepared this book. She spent hours going through her extensive collection to find some of the hard to locate foreign dolls so that I could include them in this book. Thanks to Faith Wagner, Helen Vuckovich, and Cathy Beaulieu who have purchased many Japanese and European dolls for me, Iris Lehmbach from Germany, Angelika Kercher, also from Germany, Siw Arvidsson from Sweden, and Sue Munt from Australia.

Many thanks to Kathy and Marianne for assisting in removing the dolls and fashions from their boxes and later re-packaging them, and helping haul most of the dolls featured in this book up to Margo's in Santa Barbara for their photo sessions. Also thanks to Kathy for helping with many of the menial tasks and supporting me throughout this project in so many ways. Thanks to Karen Caviale of *Barbie Bazaar* for first encouraging me to write about Barbie doll!

Thanks to Margo Rana for encouraging me to work on this exciting project and for her wonderful photography. A special thank you to Annette Nott of Annette & Friends Collectible Dolls in Westminister, California for typing the preliminary manuscript.

Front Cover: Top: 1995 **Flower Date Barbie** valued at $65. See page 92 for more information. *Bottom Left:* 1998 **New Wave Barbie** valued at $195. See page 20-A for more information. *Bottom Middle:* 1992 **Party Lights** valued at $55. See page 186 for more information. *Bottom Right:* 1994 **Dancin Rap Barbie** valued at $65. See page 119-B for more information.
Title Page: 1993 **Veterinaria Barbie** valued at $150. See page 36 for more information.
Table of Contents: 1989 **Alta Costura Lia** valued at $165. See page 24 for more information.
Back Cover: 1985 **American Doll** valued at $395. See page 93 for more information.

ABOUT THE AUTHOR

Bob Gardner has been involved in the Barbie world for a number of years. As a five year staff member of *Barbie Bazaar*, Bob has authored articles on Barbie Exclusives and more recently done feature articles on Mattel's designers and staff. Each time Bob interviewed employees at El Segundo he would learn new information on the dolls, their background, and their creation. All of this he shares with you in this book.

Bob has been a California resident for the past 16 years. He left upstate New York, where his sisters used to store their Barbie dolls in the attic, which they brought with them when the family moved here. I guess you could say he grew up with Barbie. His sisters Laurie & Lynda were always dragging them out to play. Then there were Kathy's girls, Marsha, Melissa & Michelle & Marianne. They had dolls too. Bob just couldn't get away from dolls.

Bob worked in the clothing industry for years and has an eye for fashion. He worked for actress Susan Sullivan from CBS's *Falcon Crest* as a publicist. More recently he buys sells and trades at Barbie doll shows, has a space at Len & Kathy's across from Hobby City in Anaheim California, and can be found selling at Barbara Peterson's Shows at the Disney Hotel in Anaheim. He enjoys traveling, history, writing , his family, and playing "Barbie", not necessarily in that order!

Additional copies of this book may be purchased at $39.95 (plus postage and handling) from

Hobby House Press, Inc.
1 Corporate Drive
Grantsville, Maryland 21536
1-800-554-1447
or from your favorite bookstore or dealer.

INTRODUCTION

Welcome to the fascinating world of Fashion Dolls Exclusively International! I extend the invitation to visually share these fabulous dolls not commonly offered in all parts of the world. I sincerely hope that this book sparks your interest in another phase of doll collecting!

I personally started collecting international fashion dolls about ten years ago, concentrating primarily on vintage Barbie dolls and fashions from the mod era. Soon I became hooked on adding rarities and current collectible dolls and fashions to my growing collection.

After purchasing Sybil De Wein's *Encyclopedia of Barbie*, and Sybil's second book, *Collectible Barbie Dolls, 1977-1979*, I became fascinated with the chapters she devoted to the foreign market Barbie dolls, her friends, and fashions. I was amazed and excited to see so many great dolls from the '60s and '70s and fashions that I had never known to exist.

Finding and securing items from abroad was not easy. The challenge became the obsession and the finds became the thrill! Once the international bug bit me, it soon became evident that these dolls and their ensembles aptly reflected the culture, customs, and genuine appearance of the people living in each particular country. With all the joys and sur-

prises of locating previously unseen items, this has now become my favorite area of fashion doll collecting.

The history behind these fashion dolls is fascinating. Mattel has historically granted licenses to outside companies in other countries. These various companies were able to manufacture and distribute Barbie dolls and friends only in their own countries. All their doll boxes include the licensed company's logo as well as Mattel's. These licensing contracts granted more artistic freedom to the companies because foreign countries have more lenient safety laws than the U.S./Venezuela once had gorgeous dolls with wilder hair styles and more exotic facial details produced in their country by a company called Rotoplast. Rotoplast lost their license a while back and Mattel Inc. now handles Venezuelan distribution of all Mattel products, providing them with dolls identical to those in the U.S. and Europe.

In Columbia, Mattel granted a license to Dibon to manufacture and distribute their own line of Barbie dolls. In 1995 Mattel severed their agreement with Dibon and set up their own marketing and distribution facilities in Columbia. Columbia became the 36th country where Mattel actually controls and distributes their own product from production plants in Malaysia, Indonesia, China, Mexico, and Italy.

There are several countries where Mattel Inc. still grants a license to outside companies to make other Mattel owned products. Brazil, India, Peru, and the Philippines all have licenses to produce Barbie dolls as well as her friends. Each of the respective companies produce some very fascinating dolls as you will see when you turn the pages of this book.

The Estrela company in Brazil comes up with some of the greatest concepts for their dolls. These dolls also sport some of the most marvelous facial details, coifs, and ensembles. The fashions are exquisite. The finest fabrics and notions are used. No detail, like real buttons, is overlooked. The dolls themselves often have articulated hands, which are super for holding handbags, saluting, or waving, and bendable elbows. Collectors love these human elements, but unfortunately Estrela too, had to stop production of these dolls when child safety laws in Brazil became formatted

1980 **Blue Magic Barbie** from Venezuela.
For information see page 137.

4

like the ones established in the U.S. and Europe.

One of the most innovative designed dolls — Super Teen Talk Barbie doll — was released by Mattel in 1994 in countries throughout the world. This doll had a breakthrough mechanism in doll chat. With a new micro chip installed in the torso, the doll could virtually say thousands of different phrases, without almost never repeating the same thing. All the dolls were manufactured in Mattel's China plant with different dialects — Spanish for the Latin American countries, Dutch for the Netherlands, French for France, Japanese for Japan, and so on. Mattel Inc. actually had their China factory manufacture Super Teen Talk speaking Portuguese for the Estrela company. The doll was sold exclusively in Brazil. The Estrela logo was included on the box, as well as the Mattel logo. This is the first doll sold and distributed by Estrela that was not manufactured in Brazil by their own factory. So those of you with a Portuguese speaking Super Teen Talk really have something unique!

There is wide speculation that Estrela is going to lose their license. If this happens Mattel will set up their own marketing facilities there and handle distribution of their own product in this country. It will be a real loss if these unique beauties will no longer be available.

This book also includes Mattel dolls that were actually produced in Mattel owned plants, such as China, Malaysia, and Indonesia. They are the dolls you will see in the chapters on Japan, Canada, and Europe.

A special section on international fashions provides you with a small glimpse into the world of high fashion doll dress. Incredible colors, fabrics, and accessories make international dolls stunning.

Another special section is devoted to Hasbro International's Sindy doll. Originally manufactured by Pedigree, Hasbro brought new life and look to Sindy. Their strategic marketing campaign launched a real hit for the doll industry. Sindy is so popular in the UK that she has her own active member fan club and even a Sindy boutique at London's Heathrow International Airport. Sindy dolls continue to grow in immense popularity throughout Europe and sales are brisk in the U.K., Germany, Italy, Spain, Greece, France and many more. She is seeing equal popularity in

1990 **Beautiful Bows Sindy** by Hasbro.
For information see page 175.

Australia and most recently Canada.

It is common knowledge that Mattel, Inc. sees a great resemblance to their fashion icon Barbie doll in body proportions and facial mold. Mattel Inc. was successful in receiving a court injunction against Hasbro from launching their Sindy line in the U.S. several years ago. So far Sindy has not been available on U.S. store shelves. Several hobby shops and dealers across the U.S. have been importing the Hasbro Sindy doll for sale here.

It remains a mystery just how well American customers would receive Sindy if she indeed were mass marketed in the U.S.

I collect both Barbie dolls and Sindy as well as many others. Personally I feel no one has yet to come close to manufacturing as great a doll or product as Mattel, Inc. does with their world famous Barbie doll!

When I started this project, I planned to show you a complete and comprehensive book on a good portion of exclusively international dolls. I have included countless international dolls, fashions and accessories; and after all of this, I still have many more I would like to visually share with you. There just wasn't enough room. I trust you will find this book fascinating and hope you will want to see more.

Barbie Rock Star
N/A • circa 1985 • $125

Barbie Rock Star was released in the 1980s by Top Toys of Argentina. This doll is a variation of the American Rocker series. There are similarities in the style, fabric, face paint and hair. The main difference is Rock Star Barbie doll has colorful carnation red jacket and red and gold tights.

Felices Fiestas Barbie
#8890 • 1990 • $150

Felices Fiestas Barbie doll is Argentina's version of the American Happy Holidays Series. This doll was made by former Mattel licensee, Top Toys. Barbie doll wears a deep pink spandex bodysuit with an iridescent white pearl skirt, very much like Crystal Barbie (see page 138) doll's dress. Felices Fiestas has a deep rose satin insert down the front of the skirt that is trimmed with silver braid to match the trim on her faux fur stole.

Cor Do Verão Barbie
#104021 • circa 1980s • $100

Barbie doll will stay cool wearing this three-piece cotton cabana short set. This little stripe and polka dot playsuit is an unusual pink, pale yellow, and goldenrod color combination. The duffel bag in matching stripe has the Barbie signature "B" on it.

Cor Do Verão Barbie
#105001 • circa 1980s • $175

Barbie doll is ready to tour Rio in a smart sportswear set of navy print clamdiggers, yellow knit halter top, and yellow and marine blue striped cabana vest. All shopping treasures can be stowed away in this large tote bag. *Courtesy of Alice Azpeitia.*

Cor Do Verão Barbie
#105004 • circa 1980s • $175

Dressed in a white nylon swimsuit with a tropical print wrap skirt of purple, white and deep pink, this doll with her platinum colored hair and full, curly bangs is a winner! Have you ever seen those sandals? I haven't. The cool Verão mirrored sunglasses are perfect at the shore. Barbie doll's articulated hands would be wonderful to hold a beach bag, except the strap is so long on the bag that she would be dragging it through the sand at the beach. *Courtesy of Alice Azpeitia.*

Cor Do Verão Barbie
#105022 • late 1980s • $125

This Barbie doll is as summery-fun as the one on the left. The oversized tote bag has Rio embossed across the top to match the Rio script on the doll's orange and yellow striped T-shirt.

Bridal Barbie
#105036 • circa 1980s • $150

This classic chantilly lace bridal gown is very appealing and would look wonderful on brides of all ages. With such an elaborate floral lace gown, it is appropriate that Barbie doll would select a simple illusion veil to cover her fabulous two-tone hair.

Bridal Barbie
#105057 • circa late 1980s • $150

This bride doll is very similar to the one on the left in that the gown is multi-tiered and is also made of chantilly lace and the veil is simple in design and construction. At first glance you might think they are the same doll, but look again.

Bridal Barbie
#105020 • circa 1988 • $150

Brazilian doll collectors must love old fashion bride dolls! Every year, without fail, Estrela offers a new bride doll. This particular doll wears a full lace sleeveless gown with a pink Swiss dot veil and gloves. This doll has ash blonde hair and articulated wrists.

Moda Festa Barbie

The translation for Moda Festa is "party fashion". There are seven dolls in the series.

This lavender and purple metallic bodice and chiffon skirt are perfect for the dance floor. Moda Festa's gown is lessened with the inexpensive faux-fur wrap. The silver metallic shoes make up for this fashion error. *Doll courtesy of Judy Schizas.*

Moda Festa Barbie
#105053 • circa 1980s • $175

This pink and gold marble print satin gown with two tiers of ruffles is perfect for any party. The doll's shoulders are cuddled with a cascade of pink chiffon. The doll has articulated wrists and metallic pumps.

Moda Festa Barbie
#105054 • 1989 • $150

This doll is a shimmering beauty when a spot of color is added to her black calf-length dress. A necklace with a hint of jewels accents her eyes. The doll's natural hair wave makes it easy to comb and style.

Moda Festa Viky
#105405 • 1989 • $150

Viky is the only other non Barbie doll in this series. She is particularly unique and rare in this raspberry lace cocktail dress. Look at the flawless facial paint, chestnut eyes and raspberry lips. The doll's beautiful ash blonde hair is thick and luscious.

Moda em dobro Ken
#105321 • late 1980s • $125

Dressed in black pleated trousers, white turtleneck shirt with a "Ken" emblem, a red knit hooded jacket, and a black faux leather belt complete with a brass buckle, this doll wears one of the finest quality fashions ever produced. The style is comparable to that of Benetton sportswear. The doll carries a contrasting duffel bag with real working buckle closure. Extra sweat pants are included. The plaid scarf around the doll's neck coordinates with Barbie doll's skirt. Ken, what a doll!

Moda em dobro Barbie
#105026 • circa 1987 • $125

This doll has extra thick blonde two-tone hair with appealing tight little curls. An eggplant-colored jacket is contrasted with a pink nylon scarf and printed mini dress with a short ruffled print overskirt. This doll comes with two pairs of shoes: one black, one pink. *Courtesy of Judy Schizas.*

Moda em dobro Barbie
#105025 • 1989 • $125

Our gal is ready for a day at the country club, sporting a classic red tartan plaid pleated skirt and a high quality green knit turtleneck top with a golf motif on the chest. An extra pair of pants in this package allows for two different fashion looks! Moda em dobro has a chic white felt hat with red ribbon trim and lace-up boots that were available with vintage Barbie doll fashions in the U.S. in the '70s and recently re-introduced here!

Noite de Gala Barbie
#105180 • 1986 • $150

The translation for this doll is "night of the party". The doll's calf-length dress is red chiffon with gold lurex threads. The bodice is a one shoulder style with gold braid accent. *Courtesy of Carolyn Klemovec.*

Night and Day Barbie
#105175 • circa 1987 • $125

Night and Day Barbie doll by Estrela is the same name used on a 1980s doll here in the U.S. Neither of these doll outfits share any likenesses. This doll wears a nylon print sheath of soft pastels with a mauve suede trench coat with buttons and a large belt. For day wear, a sporty blue skirt, vest, red tights, and striped top were included. This doll is wearing Barbie doll's vintage 1970s lace-up boots. *Courtesy of Judy Schizas.*

Glamour Barbie
#105019 • 1988 • $195

Gaze upon this luscious creation by Estrela in a seldom seen color of bright canary yellow. This beautiful, billowy gown of yellow chiffon layers has a matching ruffled wrap to keep shoulders warm on cooler Brazilian evenings. The shoes are the gold metallic pumps similar to those utilized on the Gold Bob Mackie Barbie doll. This gem also has articulated wrists.

Glamour Barbie
#105033 • 1989 • $175

Glamour Barbie doll puts on the latest gown for a big night out with her date. This chiffon gown of pastel-pink and seafoam floral design has a matching wrap attached by a rose to the portrait collar. The doll's hair is extremely long and simply worn. The wrists are articulated.

Glamour Barbie
#105038 • 1989 • $150

Hair is very important to Barbie doll. This green-eyed doll has blonde hair streaked with platinum arranged in a wonderful top-knot. The glamourous ensemble includes a plum satin skirt with a smart purple and silver textured jacket with braided trim and metallic pumps.

Charme em Lingerie Barbie
#105038 • 1988 • $75

What a charming, child-like facial expression! This nylon lace peignoir set is made of very high quality nylon. The pink fluffy scuffs are adorable.

Noite de Sonhos Barbie
#105091 • 1989 • $150

A feminine navy gown with three tiers of white tulled chiffon and navy bow with silk accent under the chin softens her face. Silver jewelry and metallic shoes add just enough flair to make this doll a perfect 10. *Courtesy of Judy Schizas.*

New Wave Barbie
#105006 • 1988 • $195

MTV watch out! Barbie doll will rock your socks off. Underneath a silver mini skirt are a pair of purple, blue and white lace slacks. The lamé top with big puffy sleeves and yellow stars give New Wave Barbie doll a very futuristic flare. Her hair has mounds of curls in an unusual pastel combination of pink, blue and yellow.

The box shows many other dolls. Could they have been the answer to the U.S. Barbie and the Rockers series?

New Wave Barbie
#105008 • 1988 • $165

The pink satin top, canary-yellow vest, iridescent mini skirt with sheer nylon hose are nice, but are not New Wave's most interesting asset. It's the hair that is amazing. Those curly-locks are a removable hairpiece. The doll has a blue and peach chiffon scarf to hold her wig in place. Underneath that abundant head of hair, is guess what? More hair. The articulated wrists help hold her microphone. The doll's elbows also bend allowing more play possibilities.

Rock Star Viky
#105401 • circa 1989 • $165

Circa before the date in this case means that Estrela did not put a year on their box. This was done intentionally to give each doll longer shelf-life or longer selling time. Viky doll is a welcome addition to The Sensations, Barbie and the Rockers, or New Wave series. The doll's perky little black leatherette skirt with coordinating pink and black dot top and leggings reflect a hip but conservative appeal. Viky and all the other Rock Star dolls come with: necklace, earrings, metallic shoes, microphone, and guitar.

Rock Star Lia
#105411 • circa 1989 • $150

Barbie doll's Brazilian friend Lia doll is doing a video for her latest hit single. Lia doll's stage outfit resembles the U.S. 1980s Barbie and the Sensations group rather than the American Rockers. This skirt has music notes similar to the Sensation fashions. The bodice of the dress is iridescent. The peplum skirt and jacket are pumpkin-orange and are the same fabric. The lace net stockings are patterned and the earrings, necklace, and shoes are dyed to match.

Passeio Barbie
#105029 • 1989 • $165

Brunettes are not common place in Brazil. Passeio Barbie doll's stylish *haute couture* khaki and red, all-weather coat is appropriate any time, anywhere. The doll has a matching red hat, faux reptile purse and matching belt, brown lace up boots, a red and white blouse and panties underneath. Strangely, this doll came without a skirt.

Passeio Viky
#105402 • 1989 • $145

Viky with her green eyes, freckles and wavy red hair is one of Barbie doll's many friends! A white nylon lace top accents the black and white polka-dot skirt with a dramatic red flower at the waist. Viky has those wonderful articulated wrists. This doll was also Mattel USA's gift to all convention attendees at the 1989 National Barbie Doll Convention held in Garden Grove, California. Judy Schizas of Mattel, USA was instrumental in getting 600 of these dolls inported to the U.S.

Festas Barbie
#105098 • 1989 • $165

A vision of beauty indeed! Festas Barbie doll is garbed in a graduated petal skirt and iridescent bodice with ruffled sleeves. The doll's accessories include: silver metallic pumps, a large pink and silver necklace, silver ring, and earrings.

Alta Costura Barbie
#105058 • 1989 • $150

One of seven fashions in the series, this particular Alta Costura doll wears an unusual electric blue chiffon and lace dress. The two-tone chiffon sash cinches at the waist and then flows down the front of the dress. Estrela is known for their fabulous metallic pumps. They simply glitter.

Alta Costura Lia
#105414 • 1989 • $165

Even in Brazil, Barbie doll has friends. Lia doll, made of the highest quality imaginable, has the Whitney face mold. The fabric used for this *haute couture* ensemble is top notch. A dusty blue knit skirt with dusty blue, pink, yellow, and green paisley knit bodice and over-skirt rival any U.S. dressed doll. A chic brimmed hat, complete with wired insert, is sure to make Lia doll a runway hit at any fashion show. White pearl jewelry and silver metallic pumps complete the look. Very rare.

Alta Costura Barbie
#105061 • 1989 • $195

Barbie doll sports a top-of-the line Estrela design that is similar to those great European Haute Couture or Pret-A-Porter fashions collectors clamor after. This doll dons a loose fitting lamé jacket with fold button closure, leopard print faux-sueded skirt, black hose, matching black pumps, and a fantastic leather-look purse with lamé trim. A huge gold-link chain necklace accents the fashion.

Alta Costura Barbie
#105063 • 1989 • $165

WOW! Estrela offered a chic, short hair style Barbie doll with ash blonde layered hair. This doll wears a black strapless nylon sheath dress, matching scarf, black hose, and a most fashionable jacket of tan poplin. The jacket has large buttons and pockets and is trimmed with a leopard print hood and cuffs.

Amigos Da Selva Viky
#105404 • 1989 • $195

Amigos Da Selva, translates to "Friends of the Jungle". Viky doll's American friends Barbie, Ken and Kira dolls were known in the U.S. as Animal Lovin'. This doll has very rare chestnut brown hair and is dressed in a yellow tricot skirt, leopard print halter top and matching headband. The doll came with the most adorable little lion cub.

Esporte Total Viky
#105407 • 1989 • $100

Viky wears a dark turquoise tricot one piece swimsuit with bold floral patterned pink, yellow, lavender, and turquoise slacks. A matching large floral carry bag completes this playclothes ensemble. Viky doll's hair is a lovely shade which emphasizes those cute freckles, brown eyes, and rose lips.

Super Star Lara
#105425 • 1989 • $125

Brazil's Super Star Series is a delightful version of the U.S.'s Lights & Lace series. Estrela chose Kira and Lara, as Barbie doll's friends, while in the U.S. her friends were Teresa and Christie. Lara's blue nylon and lace outfit is similar to Kira's (see page 28). Her hair is an unusual shade of brown. The look on her face makes you think that she takes her rock-star performance very seriously.

Super Star Barbie
#104420 • 1990 • $65

This doll's dress is not as full as the American version and face paint and eye make-up are more subtle. The plastic knob at her waist when turned lights up!

Super Star Kira
#105440 • 1989 • $150

This Kira with dark skin and silver eyeshadow is most unusual. The doll is outfitted in a bright yellow and peach lace ensemble. What an exotic beauty! Extremely rare. *Courtesy of Judy Schizas.*

Primavera Verão Barbie
#105083 • circa 1990s • $95

Primavera Verão Barbie doll's dress is one of the softest, most feminine party dresses she owns. The China blue paisley chiffon overskirt covers a deeper blue above-the-knee straight skirt. There is a matching blue bow sash at the waist. Silver pumps and matching jewelry are the perfect finishing touches.

Primavera Verão Skipper
#104224 • circa 1990s • $65

Skipper doll's sweet little dress with striped skirt accents Primevera Barbie doll's striped top. They will attend the luncheon together. The bodice on Skipper doll's dress is as sparkly as her eyes. The carnation on the doll's left shoulder also adds a hint of glitter. Together, these two dolls make a darling display.

Primavera Verão Barbie

#105087 • circa 1990s • $125

Barbie doll is ready for an informal luncheon with the girls with this one piece jumpsuit of white linen-like trousers. A pink and white floral jacket covers a little pink and white striped top. A strawberry pink chiffon scarf tied around the doll's waist dresses up the ensemble. Accessories include: a necklace, earrings, ring, white pumps, and a white purse.

Outono Inverno Lia
#105416 • early 1990s • $150

Lia doll is wearing a fall fashion that makes her one of the greatest releases from Estrela. Lia doll's black faux suede skirt with multi-striped mock-turtleneck provides warmth on brisk fall days. A white felt hat with gold braid trim frames this little cutie's face, drawing attention to her big brown eyes. Black lace-up boots keep her tootsies warm.

Outono Inverno Barbie
#105088 • early 1990s • $159

Lia doll (left) has a nice fall outfit and so does Outono Inverno Barbie doll. This doll has chosen a gold knit dress with a beautiful burgundy, gold, black, beige and olive printed jacket to keep her warm on her way to the symphony.

Glitter Look Barbie

#105540 • circa 1990 • $65

With a deep rich tan like this, Barbie doll is a tropical beauty from head to toe. Glitter Look Barbie doll's vibrant multi-colored two-piece dress with pink chiffon overskirt shows off that fabulous sun tan. The Glitter Look dolls came with a bottle of glitter cream that could be put either on the dolls, in the hair, or on the clothes. Many mother's found their children glittering too!

Festa De Casamento Skipper
#104227 • 1991 • $75

Wedding Day Midge doll and her entourage were widely sold throughout the U.S. Festa De Casamento Skipper was Brazil's addition to the wedding party. Estrela also offered a wedding party which included Bride Viky, Groom Alan, Best Man Ken, Bridesmaid Barbie, and the flower girl Skipper you see here dressed in powder-blue Swiss dot with lace trim, carrying a sweet floral bouquet.

Festa De Casamento Ken
#105340 • 1991 • $75

Estrela of Brazil had Best Man Ken doll opt for a sharp iridescent burgundy tuxedo and pink shirt with silver tie for Viky and Alan dolls most important day. Unfortunately I do not have the other three dolls in the wedding party, but you can see them on the back of the box. Their resemblance to the American version is obvious.

Noiva Romantica Barbie
#105584 • 1992 • $150

Noiva Romantica is Estrela's version of Wedding Fantasy found in the U.S. The lace quality of this June bride is exceptional. The doll's hair, make-up, and eye color are wonderful changes from the ordinary. The chantilly lace dress is not floral as you saw on the previous brides (*see pages 10-11*). Noiva Romantica's gown has a wedding-bow pattern. The veil is the same design that came with Barbie doll's very first wedding gown back in 1959.

Skipper

#104225 • 1993 • $65

Throughout the world, Barbie doll's little sister is Skipper doll. This doll was exclusive to the Brazilian market. With full long hair and a cute little two-tone blue dress, this doll is perfectly outfitted for school, play, church or party.

Tenis & Jeans Barbie
#104410 • 1993 • $75

The three Tenis & Jean dolls that were available in Brazil were Estrela's version of the U.S.'s All American dolls. Tenis & Jeans Barbie doll wears denim with pink and white stripe accents. The American version had red and white stripes. The high-top sneakers say "Barbie"; All American Barbie doll's say "Reebok". The doll's platinum hair is striking with a wonderful tan. The blue ponytail wrap served as bracelets in the American regular line series, Wet and Wild.

Veterinaria Barbie
#104430 • 1993 • $150

Veterinaria Barbie doll was released in 1993. The Estrela Company was the first to make Barbie doll a veterinarian. Mattel USA did not have a veterinarian doll until 1996. This doll has the Day-to-Night concept — once the doctor's coat is removed, Barbie doll is ready for a fund raiser for the Humane Society. This rare doll comes with a fabulous dog. Notice the first place ribbon, which the author won in the Foreign Barbie doll category at the 1993 National Barbie Convention in Baltimore, Maryland.

Sonho De Ferias Barbie
#105067 • 1993 • $65

Dressed in a sporty denim skirt and coordinated paisley jacket trimmed in yellow, Sonho De Ferias Barbie doll is ready for a day at the fair. This box comes shrink-wrapped, so, we chose not to disturb the packaging. Estrela is known for doing this, mainly for security reasons when traveling through customs. *Courtesy of Margo Rana.*

Charme Tropical Barbie
#105502 • 1993 • $65

Charme Tropical Barbie doll was Estrela's answer to Mattel's European release known as Tahiti Barbie doll, stock #2093 (see page 61). The hair styles are the same on both dolls, but the face paint and colors of the two are extraordinarily different.

Moda Flor Barbie
#105586 • 1993 • $125

Moda Flor Barbie doll was Estrela's version of the Mattel produced Party Changes/Party Kleding #2545 (available only in Europe and U.S. specialty stores). The similarities are striking, but not exact. This Brazilian doll has a dark suntan, metallic jewelry, magenta metallic pumps to match, and carries a bouquet, whereas Party Changes had a flower in her hair.

3 Estilos Barbie
#105367 • 1994 • $95

3 Estilos Barbie doll is extremely similar to the U.S.'s American Beauty Queen doll. You can see on the box how she got her name; the outfit transforms into two other styles. 3 Estilos differs from American Beauty Queen Barbie doll in that this gown is made from a heavier quality fabric and is a bit brighter in color. The main difference is that this Brazilian doll does not come with a beauty pageant banner. *Courtesy of Judy Schizas.*

Eco-Camping Barbie
#105575 • 1994 • $65

Barbie and Ken dolls went camping in the U.S. in 1994 in a collection called Camping Fun. Brazil had their own camping version with emphasis on ecology. Barbie doll's backpack and jacket were made of poplin, whereas the Mattel USA version was a different fabric. *Courtesy of Judy Schizas.*

Eco-Camping Ken
#105576 • 1994 • $75

The Mattel USA Camping Ken doll was difficult to find in some parts of the United States. If you had a hard time finding him, imagine trying to find Eco Ken doll, whose outfit is entirely different from the U.S. doll. *Courtesy of Judy Schizas.*

Sonho de Noiva Barbie
#1054423 • 1994 • $150

Sonho de Noiva Barbie doll has a simple, airy chiffon skirted gown with several layers. The bodice is printed and a pale pink sash has been added at the waist to match the pink rose corsage. You can envision this doll gliding down the aisle to meet her one and only Ken doll.

Buque & Grinalda Barbie
#105639 • 1995 • $150

This is one of the prettiest Estrela brides ever! Barbie doll's pure white contemporary gown with lace trim is striking next to a deep tan. The three-rose bouquet isn't wilting, Margo forgot to prop them up before taking her picture. *Courtesy of Judy Schizas.*

Estrela Barbie Doll House

This is a very unique, absolutely wonderful Estrela Barbie doll house. The frame is made of real wood and the rooms are colorful and spacious, making it easy to get the dolls and furniture in and out. There is good visibility to all the rooms and the dolls. The dolls standing in the house were all manufactured by Estrela and are many collector's favorites. *Estrela House from the collection of Margo Rana.*

Club California Barbie
#4439 • 1987 • $65

This gift set was released for Canada only. Barbie doll comes with a bilingual cassette tape with songs that were recorded especially for the Canadian market. This same doll was released in the U.S. in a slim-sized package and called California Barbie. The cassette tape included with the U.S. version was an all-new specially-written song about Barbie doll, by the long-time California surf group, the Beach Boys. *Courtesy of Margo Rana.*

Skating Star/Etoile Du Patin
#4547 • 1987 • $95

An exclusive Mattel Canada released for the 1988 Winter Olympics in Calgary. Skating Star has a short skirt, Olympic seal decals, and a punch-out gold medal. This doll is very similar to the Sears customized Star Dream Barbie doll.

Lights & Lace, Dentellés et Étincelles Barbie
#9725 • 1990 • $45

This doll was available in the U.S. as Lights and Lace. Dressed in pale pink chantilly lace, her face paint is more subtle than the American version. As in the U.S., Dentellés et Étincelles also had Christie and Teresa dolls in the series.

Beauty Queen/Reine De Beauté
#3137 • 1991 • $55

This version of American Beauty Barbie doll is a Canadian release purchased at Toys R Us, Toronto where they use green stickers. The doll's banner says "Beauty Queen - Reine de Beauté" instead of "American Beauty Queen".

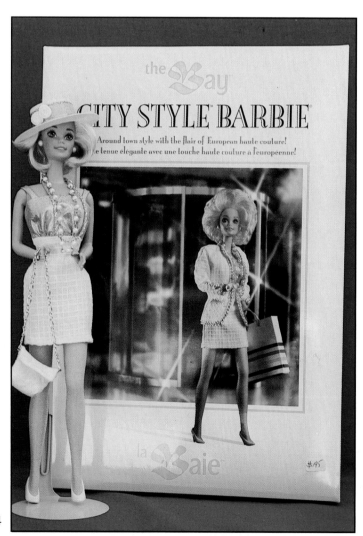

The Bay City Style Barbie
#10149 • 1993 • $195

This is Hudson Bay's (a Canadian department store) first customized Barbie doll. This doll is the City Style doll from the American Classique Collection. Janet Goldblatt was the Mattel designer for this doll. Mattel had manufactured a lot of City Style Barbie dolls and offered it to Hudson Bay Company with new packaging showing Barbie doll coming out of the entrance of one of the their stores carrying a Bay shopping bag that was created just for her.

3 Looks, 3 Modas, 3 Tenues Mode Barbie
#12339 • 1994 • $55

3 Modas Barbie doll was found primarily in Canada. This doll was also featured in Mattel's Scandinavian catalog. 3 Looks wears a pink and silver gown that is identical in fabric and style to the U.S.'s American Beauty Queen, which was made in blue. 3 Looks wears unusual crystal-like earrings. This fashion outfit comes with removable pieces to create different looks.

Rouli Barbie et Son Chein Roulant
#12098 • 1994 • $150

This is Zeller's (a Canadian chain store) first customized doll. It is reported that only 2,000 gift sets were manufactured — they sold out immediately. This doll set was probably manufactured to compete with Sindy's walking dog gift set (*see* page 178). Canada's Barbie doll was dressed in rollerblade fashion #4850 that sold in the U.S. in a blister-pack and in Europe and Canada in a closed box, as shown on the bottom left. A roll-along puppy was also sold separately.

Governor's Ball/Bal Du Gouveneur
#14010 • 1995 • $125

Here is the second customized Barbie doll made for Canada's Hudson Bay Department Store. There were very few of these dolls available in this packaging. This doll is the 1995 JC Penney Royal Enchantment doll. Both dolls share the same Mattel stock number. There are no JC Penney stores in Canada, therefore this doll was offered as their exclusive, complete with a replica parchment invitation to the Governor's Ball. The sealed box shows Barbie doll descending a staircase carpeted in the same texture and color as the doll's dress. This gem was designed by Ann Driskill who is Mattel's honored 1997 Classique designer!

Ruffle Fun, Frou-Frou Barbie
#15802 • 1996 • $35

Mattel/Canada's Frou-Frou Barbie doll was Zeller's second customized Barbie doll. Ruffle Fun was also available in the U.S. wearing the same style, different color (yellow and pink) dress, as opposed to the purple, pink and yellow you see here.

Arcadian Court Barbie
#62889 • 1996 • $150

Arcadian Court is the third customized Mattel/Canada produced doll for the Hudson Bay Department stores. Within two weeks of her release, the doll was no longer available. The doll was very similar to the Sears Ribbon and Roses. As a result, Arcadian Court Barbie doll was removed from the shelves in the Bay stores. In addition to the packaging being different, this doll's dress had a short bow at the waist and came without a necklace. The set came with the Arcadian Court logo on it and had a cute High Tea Menu and table cloth. There were only 2900 pieces produced and more than half of those were recalled. What a shame!

Chantal Goya
#8935-63 • 1979 • $150

Chantal Goya was a very prominent French recording artist, known for her children's songs. Mattel/France recognized this artist by designing a doll in an extrememly accurate likeness of Chantal. The doll wears an exact replica of a rust floral peasant dress with lace collar that Chantal herself had performed in. Chantal is wearing that same dress on the back of the doll box. Mattel/France also sold a complete line of Chantal Goya doll fashions. It stated on the boxes that Barbie doll could share them too. *Courtesy of Margo Rana.*

Fruhlingszauber Barbie
#7546 • 1983 • $150

Mattel, Germany had this wonderful doll made exclusively for distribution in Germany. Barbie doll is a breath of springtime, decked-out in a sugar-sheer organdy gown of purple, pink, and white. A beautiful ruffled wrap envelopes her shoulders and a big brim straw hat adds the finishing touches. This fashion, part of a 3 fashion collector series of fancy gowns, was released in the U.S. in 1983 in a window-box style package with stock #7093. *Courtesy of Margo Rana.*

California Skipper
#4440 • 1987 • $55

Skipper doll was missing from the U.S.'s 1987 doll series known as California. Designed for release in Europe and Canada, California Skipper doll wears a marine blue tricot swimsuit with yellow stripe coveralls with splashes of 45 records and musical notes. A striped backpack, boom box, Frisbee, sun visor, and California banner are included with this doll.

Bobby Bi Bops
#4960 • 1987 • $175

Bobby Bi Bops is the exclusive male member of Barbie & the Sensations for select European markets and mainly was found in France. Interestingly, not only was Christie omitted from Europe, but Mattel changed names too. Our Becky became Bibi and Bopsy became Becky. This Bobby doll is a great addition and has that great face mold (the one that the Marine Ken should have had been made from). The doll wears a purple metallic jumpsuit with a silver top and a great musical note baseball jacket of pearl white and florescent yellow. Shoes, socks, microphone, and dark shades are his accessories. Extremely rare.

Bobby Bi Bops Stage Wardrobe
#4990 • 1987 • $95

Equally as rare and almost impossible to find is this Bobby Bi Bops stage wardrobe. The back of the box shows the five female fashions and his sole one. His fashion consists of electric blue and fluorescent yellow jumpsuit, wild metallic print jacket, cummerbund, bow tie, shoes, and socks.

Barbie Chic
#60251 • 1988 • $75

Barbie Chic was made in Spain for Mattel/Spain. Very few dolls are actually produced in Spain. Barbie Chic wears a cool crepe dress of white with emerald green polka dots. The hemline is a balloon effect with elasticized hem, so one can raise or lower Barbie doll's hemline.

Voyage Barbie
#1007 • 1990 • $95

Shown here is an unusual gift set made by Mattel only for the European market. The doll wears a purple print ruffled skirt, white velcro crop-top, purple print cotton vest trimmed with pink velcro and comes with large velcro storage bag to place Barbie doll in. There are extra velcro attached accessories to add to Barbie doll's velcro top and vest. This nice set is a great concept for a child.

5th Anniversario em Portugal Barbie
#6139 • 1989 • $195

5th Anniversario Em Portugal was created by Tonio Augusties, a noted Portuguese fashion designer. This doll was manufactured in the Mattel plant in Spain and was exclusive to Portugal in celebration of Mattel's 5th year of operation in that country. Barbie doll's blue-gray and white foil fabric dress has three layers of crisp crinoline to make the skirt stand out. The dress is topped with a matching bolero jacket. A self-fabric bow adds just the right touch. Inside the garment is a label that reads "Disento Original Barbie". This doll, available for a very short time, is extremely rare.

Benetton Ken
#9406 • 1990 • $75

The first year of production, the Benetton Barbie doll series was a Mattel main-line offering. They were shown in the dealer catalogs in 1991. The U.S. catalog showed all five dolls but stated that Ken and Teresa dolls were not available in the U.S. The Kira doll offered here in the U.S., was called Marina in Europe. Ken doll wears a casual South American inspired outfit. The fabric of the T-shirt and jacket is an extremely colorful abstract print. The trousers are made of tangelo polished cotton which match the doll's felt hat and socks perfectly. Few Ken dolls come with hats; with Benetton Ken, not only do you get a hat, but a bandanna too. *Courtesy of Margo Rana.*

Benetton Shopping Ken
#4876 • 1991 • $75

Benetton Shopping Ken was only sold in select European countries. Barbie doll in this series was only sold in Europe and in specialty doll shops in the U.S. This Ken doll with frosted-painted hair, wears a burnt sienna suedette bomber jacket trimmed with orange and yellow striped collar and cuffs. The pleated trousers of red-wale and the T-shirt with "UCB", United Colours of Benetton logo, make this doll the kind of Ken doll you could only get from Benetton. *Courtesy of Margo Rana.*

Benetton Teresa
#9408 • 1990 • $125

This is one of the cutest Teresa dolls Mattel has manufactured. Although only available in Europe, this doll is highly sought after by American collectors because of her rich face paint. Teresa doll's sportswear was designed especially for the Benetton Clothing Company. Underneath a jewel-tone multi-print jacket is a tangerine turtleneck. The doll has blue shorts, backpack, leggings, red socks, and yellow sneakers which match dandelion yellow earrings. *Courtesy of Margo Rana.*

Benetton Shopping Teresa
#4880 • 1991 • $175

This seldom seen Benetton Shopping Teresa doll is the hardest to find because of a low production level and limited availability. Underneath a green jumper, is a blue and green argyle turtleneck that matches the leggings. This fabric was used in 1992 on Golf Date Barbie doll. The bright yellow jacket is winter-quilted. Accessories include: yellow socks, turquoise sneakers, green and yellow hat, and large hoop earrings as were worn by all the Shopping dolls. *Courtesy of Margo Rana.*

Benetton Shopping Marina
#4898 • 1991 • $165

Benetton Shopping Marina, only released in select European countries, starts the second Benetton series. This very rare and now almost impossible to find doll is dressed in a drawstring jacket of magenta polished cotton with a white, pink and seafoam green plaid lining to match the skirt. The outfit is complete with magenta leggings, plaid socks, sneakers, and a ski cap with a jewel-jade pompom. Benetton Marina's clothes are as cheerful as the clothing you would find in any Benetton clothing store.

Benetton Shopping Christie
#4887 • 1991 • $95

Of the two Benetton Christie dolls, this is the harder of the two to find. She is the only one in the series that has a heavy knit sweater like the ones Benetton is famous for making for adults. It is a red and yellow striped, long sleeve mock-turtleneck. Christie doll is wearing a peacock blue knit skirt and matching shawl. The leggings are orange and the sneakers are red. The colors all come together with a floppy red and blue hat. *Courtesy of Margo Rana.*

Dream Bride Barbie
#5466 • 1991 $165
This Dream Bride Barbie doll was made by Mattel and was released in only a few European countries. This one came from France. Dream Bride, in a gown embellished with pearls and sequins, is the prettiest Bride doll Mattel has manufactured to date. This doll is extremely rare.

Ultra Hair Whitney
#7735 • 1991 • $85
Ultra Hair Whitney doll was manufactured for European distribution. This is the last Whitney doll produced by Mattel to date. In Europe this ultra hair series had the following dolls: Ultra Hair Whitney, Blonde Barbie and Ken doll. Our American brunette Totally Hair Barbie doll wore the identical aqua, purple and pink Emilio Pucci inspired fabric that you see Whitney doll wearing. This doll is very rare. The U.S. also had a Totally Hair Skipper and Courtney dolls but these were a customized exclusive and sold only at Toys 'R Us.

Barbie Style
#2453 • 1992 • $25

This is one of two Barbie Style dolls available in Canada, Mexico, and Europe in 1993. This doll is very similar to Woolworth's 1992 Special Expression doll. Differences in this European style doll include: no earrings nor hair bow, and interfacing fabric inside the neckline and shoulders of heavy blue nylon.

Earring Magic Midge
#7018 • 1992 • $65

Mattel Inc. produced Midge doll in a blue dress for the European market only. The U.S. Midge doll was released with stock #10256 and wore a yellow dress. This European version has a blue dress worn by a brunette Earring Magic Barbie doll sold in the U.S. European Midge doll wears gold accent jewelry, while the U.S. yellow version wears copper-tone jewelry. This blue dress doll is very rare and difficult to find.

Tahiti Barbie
#02093 • 1992 • $25

This doll was produced by Mattel for Europe and Mexico. The doll is simple, yet elegant in a bold abstract geometric print knit sheath with her hair worn in a ponytail high on the top of her head.

Allegra
#05537 • 1992 • $75

Here is one of several riding horses Mattel manufactured for exclusive European distribution. This one was made in Italy where several of the Mattel accessories are actually manufactured. The horse "whinnies" when one puts Barbie doll on the saddle. The horse has ribbons and barrettes that can be shared with Barbie doll. Allegra also sports a beautiful white mane. Very rare!

Butterfly
#10082 • 1992 • $65

Butterfly horse appeared in Europe in 1992 and was manufactured in Mattel's plant in Italy. Her butterflies detach and can be worn as barrettes in a little girl's hair. Rare!

Disney Weekend Barbie
#10722 • 1993 • $65

Disney Barbie doll is ready for Splash Mountain, wearing a cotton dress of black and white polka-dot, sleeves with ruffled hemline. The cuffs and neckline are purple ribbed knit and Mickey Mouse is emblazoned across her bodice. Disney Weekend Barbie doll would not be complete unless she was sporting mouse ears! *Courtesy of Margo Rana.*

Disney Weekend Barbie
#10723 • 1993 • $75

This is one of several Disney-theme dolls produced for international release only. All carry the Euro-Disney logo on the back of all their boxes. They have been sold in Euro-Disney, France at the theme park and could also be found in department stores throughout Europe, Australia, and even Mexico. This one is a gift set. Our doll is wearing a pink cotton skirt and a lime, pink and orange knit T-shirt with a cute print of Mickey and Minnie Mouse. Extra clothing includes: yellow cotton pleated shorts with hot pink trim and a yellow and hot pink T-shirt with a Daisy Duck motif. Barbie doll wears the signature mouse ear hat. *Courtesy of Margo Rana.*

Deluxe Disney Weekend, Barbie and Ken Gift Set
#10724 • 1993 • $150

This is a near impossible set to find of the Euro-Disney doll line. It is very similar to the Toys 'R Us, Barbie and Friends Gift Set released in 1991. The Toys 'R Us set was manufactured in Malaysia. The rare European gift set you see here, was manufactured in 1993 in China. The Barbie doll in this package is dressed identically to the 1991 set but this doll has gorgeous face paint and lush fiber hair. Ken doll has the Alan face mold, whereas the Toys 'R Us version has the old Ken face. Skipper doll was eliminated from the European version. In both sets Barbie doll wears mouse ears. *Courtesy Margo Rana.*

Disney Fun Barbie
#12957 • 1994 • $55

This is the fourth Euro-Disney Barbie doll. Dressed in Mickey Mouse print slacks, matching jacket, a pink and white gingham check blouse, matching handkerchief, and carrying a pink suede mouse-shaped shoulder bag, this doll is ready to enjoy the rides. *Courtesy of Margo Rana.*

Naf Naf Ken
#10998 • 1993 • $65

This is one of the best Ken dolls of recent years. Ken doll wears a terrific denim suit, a yellow tank top, and a baseball cap with the Naf Naf signature print and logo. Accessories include: a great Naf Naf backpack and extra green spandex swimtrunks. The doll packaging is unique too. It is yellow, gold and pink with the Naf Naf signature colors with a pop-up carry handle on the box lid. *Courtesy of Margo Rana.*

Naf Naf Midge
#10999 • 1993 • $85

What a great addition to the Midge series! Midge doll wears a real Euro-print pantsuit (the same fabric Mattel recycled on the 1995 exclusive Toys 'R Us doll, known as International Pen Friend), a yellow tricot tank top, large Naf Naf logo bangle earrings, and a neat retro yellow logo baseball cap. An extra orange Naf Naf logo print sheath is included and a colorful logo backpack too. *Courtesy of Margo Rana.*

Naf Naf, a clothing manufacturer similar to Benetton, is known for their colorful sportswear. Ken and Midge dolls were manufactured by Mattel/China to be sold only in select European countries where Naf Naf clothing is a smash. The Barbie doll was also available in specialty stores in the U.S. All three dolls of this series had low production numbers and are very difficult to find.

Jewel and Glitter Barbie
#11185 • 1993 • $65

Mattel originally planned to release this series in the U.S. and to include three dolls. They were similar to the 1992 Paint 'N Dazzle series. Jewel and Glitter fashions in special window boxes were released domestically. They were the same fashions that Barbie, Teresa, and Shani dolls wear. Barbie doll wears a black suede mini skirt and bolero vest, both with scalloped edges. A gold lamé waistband and gold lamé tube top complete the look. *Courtesy of Margo Rana.*

Jewel and Glitter Teresa
#11214 • 1993 • $65

Teresa looks smashing with her copper color crimped hair, bright purple two-layer flared skirt, silver lamé waistband, and purple scalloped edge halter top. This doll's only accessories are silver drop earrings. Jewel Glitter Teresa doll, as did Barbie doll, came with separate packages of jewels which were to be glued on to her faux-sueded ensemble. *Courtesy of Margo Rana.*

Butterfly Prince/Schmetterling Zauber Ken
#13237 • 1994 • $45

In 1995, this doll was the match for Butterfly Barbie doll and the lead main-line entry. Only offered in Canada, Europe, and South America, this was the only year a lead Ken doll was not sold in the U.S. Butterfly Prince Ken doll has brown rooted hair and looks dashing in a black and silver glitter-stretch fabric tuxedo, white pleated shirt, pink chiffon bow tie, and matching cummerbund. The doll comes with a coordinating butterfly corsage for him to place on Barbie doll, if the two should ever meet! *Courtesy of Margo Rana.*

Dance Moves/Baila Comiigo Midge
#13085 • 1993 • $55

Dance Moves Midge doll was a nice surprise for people traveling to Canada, Europe, and South America in 1995. The U.S. received the Barbie, Teresa, and black Barbie dolls, but no Midge. The international market received the Midge doll in place of the black Barbie doll. Dance Moves Midge is dressed in blue and silver knit tights, blue and silver stretch knit top, and electric blue metallic suspender shorts. A boom box and walkman were also included. *Courtesy of Margo Rana.*

Horse Riding/Ecuestre Cavaliere Barbie
#12456 • 1994 • $65

This great doll was manufactured for release in Canada, Europe, and South America. A gymnast articulated body was used. Barbie doll looks like a real champion rider in silver jodphurs, a green, pink and blue plaid jacket with silver trim collar and matching cuffs. Mattel also manufactured a doll and horse gift set using this doll. It was originally manufactured for international distribution but available at Hills department store chain and FAO Schwarz here in the U.S. *Courtesy of Margo Rana.*

Baywatch Teresa
#13201 • 1994 • $45

Baywatch Teresa was only packaged for international release. Teresa doll and the other Baywatch dolls are photographed on the back of this imported box along with the actual cast members from the TV hit series. The U.S. boxes did not include these images. *Courtesy of Margo Rana.*

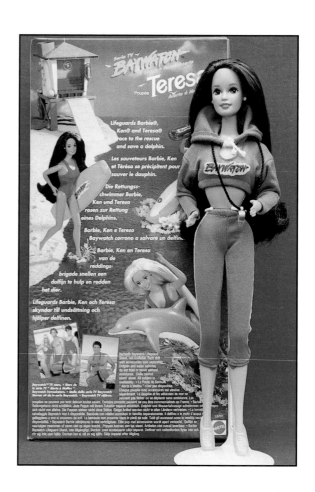

Barbie Style from Amsterdam
#N/A • 1994 • $175

This extremely rare set, made by Mattel only for the Netherlands, consists of the European style Barbie doll in a matching vinyl window box carrying case with handle, a most unique package. This one received a 1st Place Blue Ribbon at the 1994 National Barbie Doll Convention in Birmingham for the Foreign Category of dolls.

Super Star Barbie
#10592 • 1994 • $65

This Walmart customized doll was released as a regular line doll for the French market by Mattel, France. The box is in French and the Walmart logo is excluded from the box and the doll's hang tag. Several customized U.S. dolls have been found throughout Europe in different packages and/or with name changes. Very limited.

Camping Barbie Deluxe Set
#12185 • 1994 • $125

A very rare gift set made exclusively for select European countries. This camping set includes the same doll as in the individual packages, but comes with many extra accessories and a Barbie doll sized tent. Scarce and hard to find.

Magical Hair Mermaid
#11570 • 1994 • $95

This 1994 purple haired mermaid was only produced for international distribution. Magical Hair Mermaid is the prettiest one Mattel has produced to date and the only Barbie doll to date with purple hair actually made by Mattel. A treasure! *Courtesy of Margo Rana.*

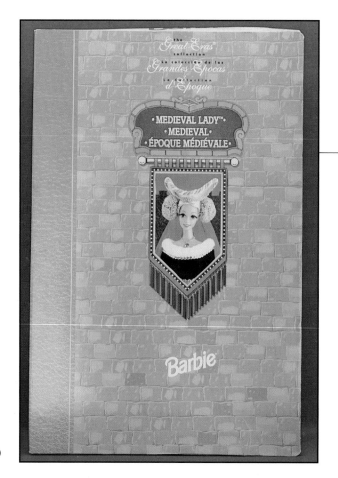

Grandes Epocas/ d'Epoque (Medieval Lady)
#12791 • 1994 • $100

When I correspond and trade with friends in several European countries, they have repeatedly told me all of our collectible dolls are in the U.S/English boxes only. Recently, while visiting Mexico, I came across this all foreign packaging of a Medieval Lady. It is in French and Spanish. It says it is for Mattel/France, Mattel/Spain, Venezuela, Chile, and Mexico. A unique find!

Happy Holidays/Gala/Festas
#12432 • 1994 • $195

This extraordinary doll, the first of an exclusive International Happy Holidays series, was designed by Mattel's ultra-hot designer, Ann Driskill. European collectors were tired of seeing our Happy Holidays dolls in magazines and waiting a year to get them. (Europe releases the U.S. Happy Holidays dolls one year later than our release.) Mattel, Inc. decided to provide them with two releases, the U.S. version and an exclusive European Happy Holidays doll. This first International Happy Holidays doll was lavishly decked out in a red flocked gown with fur collar, cuffs, hat, and tassels. Ann Driskill created a similar doll for the U.S. in 1993 called Winter Royale for wholesale clubs and specialty shops. Ann Driskill sure has a flair for designing collector's favorites!

Happy Holidays/Gala
#13354 • 1995 • $95

Gala Barbie doll is the second Happy Holidays doll for the international market. This is a re-make of Mattel designer, Geralyn Nelson's Peppermint Princess. This doll is gorgeous in a forest green velvet bodice with a white satin skirt with red, green and gold ribbon stripes. The velvet can be found in either a deep rich forest green or another paler green version.

Happy Holidays/Gala
#15816 • 1996 • $75

Mattel's third international holiday Gala Barbie doll uses the same pattern as the 1995 Winter's Eve doll that was available here in the U.S. This plaid is a true Christmas plaid of red, blue, green and gold. The doll's hair is elegantly styled, pulled back in a high, loose ponytail with ribbon to match her skirt. Green eyes with a hint of gold eyeshadow add a real sophisticated look to this beauty.

Harvey Nichols Barbie
#00175 • 1995 • $2,000

Harvey Nichols Barbie doll is one of the most elite and most difficult dolls to acquire. Released in the spring of 1995 for the prestigious Harvey Nichols store in London, Mattel/UK produced only 250 of these dolls; each came with a numbered certificate. The doll is a blonde reproduction #1 Barbie doll which is re-dressed in a sharp retro-style genuine shantung silk pink jacket that is worn over a black rayon crepe round neck sleeveless dress. Not shown are the chiffon-marabou trimmed shawl and black purse. The artwork on the box is as fabulous as the doll. There are London flair etchings on the box of Tower Bridge, Big Ben, and even a Buckingham Palace Guard. This is the doll for the collector who has got to have it all! *Courtesy of Margo Rana.*

100 Jaar Blokker Barbie
#15611 • 1995 • $95

This is the first customized doll produced for Blokker's, a department store chain in Belgium. Mattel manufactured this solely for Blokker's 100th Anniversary. Blokker Barbie doll wears the Quinceanera Teresa gown fashion by Geralyn Nelson (originally designed as a Toys 'R Us exclusive). A special 100th Anniversary hang tag with Blokker's name and logo is attached to the doll's wrists. *Courtesy of Margo Rana.*

Gardaland Barbie
#14650 • 1995 • $95

Mattel, Inc produced this very hard to obtain doll for exclusive sale in Italy's famed amusement park, GARDALAND. This special edition can be compared to those Mattel produces exclusively for the Disney theme parks. Barbie doll is ready for a long day of fun and rides, wearing a drop waist mini skirt of hot pink and black satin with contrasting ribbon trim of lime and yellow with silver star appliqués. A black spandex crop top with silver strap appliqués is also worn. A replica ticket for admission to the theme park is also included. *Courtesy of Margo Rana.*

Johnny Hallyday en Concert
#14069 • 1995 • $150

Not since 1979 when Mattel produced French singing sensation Chantal Goya, has there been another licensed celebrity "friend" for outside the U.S. Johnny Hallyday was produced by Mattel in 1995 for Mattel/France. An all new face mold was sculpted by Mattel in Mr. Hallyday's likeness. Johnny Hallyday has sold 80 million records and recorded over 50 smash hit albums in the French language. He made his debut in 1960. The doll is exceptional and wears a replica stage fashion that Hallyday actually wore on stage. It consists of black "leather" studded bell-bottom slacks, a red nylon lace-up shirt, a black and silver metallic baseball jacket, and even an earring! Johnny comes with a guitar, a microphone, and a numbered certificate of authenticity.

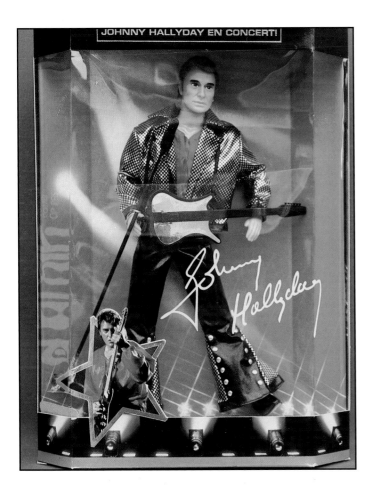

Super Gymnast Barbie
#15821 • 1996 • $55

This is Mattel's international version of the U.S.'s Olympic Barbie doll that wore the red, white and blue leotard with the Atlanta Olympic symbol. For Europe and other parts of the world, Mattel re-designed the basic concept only in aqua, hot pink, and white. Both dolls are wonderful. This version does not have the gym bag, that the U.S. version did.

West End Barbie
#15513 • 1996 • $85

This gem from London, England, was produced for Hamley's, "The Finest Toy Shop". The doll is a re-tooled version of FAO Schwarz's Shopping Spree. West End Barbie doll wears red knit slacks, an over-sized sweat shirt of white with black ribbed acrylic sleeves, neck and hem. The Hamley's logo is embossed across the front. A matching baseball cap completes this ensemble as does a great Hamley's shopping bag. This prestigious shop is located on Regent Street in London, and the Royal Family has purchased their toys there for years. The box colors and graphics add to the collectibility of this superior doll. This doll was limited to 20,000 and is hard to find. *Courtesy of Margo Rana.*

Teen Talk Barbie Doll

Shown here are Teen Talk Barbie dolls from abroad. These dolls were made in 1991 and each says six phrases. Are you wondering if any say, "Math class is tough" in their native language? All the dolls from Europe appear to be various shades of blonde. Mexico, Chile, and Venezuela have been found with various shades of red hair. There were also two hair styles and colors — dark blonde with straight to crimped hair and light blonde hair with soft curls and side braids — that were not found on U.S. dolls. The light blonde style was used on an American red-head version. Both hair styles are shown in the close-up photos.

Ich Spreche Mit Dir
MATTEL/GERMANY
#4767 • 1991 • $85

With the turquoise floral ensemble and Europe only dark blonde straight-to-crimp hair style.

Teen Talk Barbie
MATTEL/ENGLAND
#4951 • 1991 • $85

This delightful British accent, much like Princess Diana's, brings back fond memories of Barbie doll's talking British chum of the '60s, Stacey doll. This doll's hair style is the one found on the American redheads, only here she is rooted in blonde for the European market.

Mayikn Pwvn Barbie
MATTEL/GREECE
#5083 • 1991 • $150

This virtually impossible to find doll speaks Greek and is as lovely as all her other European clones.

Ik Praat Met Je Barbie
MATTEL/AMSTERDAM
#4897 • 1991 • $95

This extremely hard-to-find doll speaks Dutch.

Magica Voce Barbie
MATTEL/ITALY
#4838 • 1991 • $95

Here's a beautiful doll with a lovely Italian accent. The hair style and color are exclusive to Europe.

Je Te Parle Barbie
MATTEL/FRANCE
#4709 • 1991 • $85

This is the same doll as other European designs except the packaging is written in French.

Dulces Palabras Barbie
MATTEL/SPAIN
#4851 • 1991 • $95

Dulces Palabras was manufactured for Mattel/Spain, and consequently speaks Spanish. This doll has an exclusive dark blonde hair style found only in Europe.

Dulces Palabras
MATTEL/MEXICO, CHILE, ARGENTINA
#4851 • 1991 • $85

The box for these dolls did not have batteries installed in their backs as did many of the others.

Sprich Mit Barbie
#12373 • 1994 • $95

Here is our girl packed for Mattel/Germany and speaking German, of course. This doll came out in 1994 when the U.S. got their English speaking doll. Mattel produced several others for various countries.

De 10,000 Zinnen Barbie
#12376 • 1994 • $150

Mattel's China plant produced this doll in 1994 with her Dutch dialect for Brussels (Holland). She was very hard to find, even over there!

Conversa Contigo
#12380 • 1994 • $95

This spanish speaking version was produced by Mattel for their accounts in Mexico, Chile, and Venezuela.

Japanese Talk Barbie
#12494 • 1994 • $175

Almost everyone (airline personnel, tourists, etc.) said they could hardly find this doll when over in Japan. This doll is VERY, VERY RARE. All of Japan's Barbie doll boxes include this little paragraph "Barbie is the most beautiful and popular girl who is always leading the newest trends. She has a fun and fashionable lifestyle that you can really enjoy!"

Fala 10,000 Frases Barbie
#14127 • 1995 • $125

This doll is the one mentioned in the introduction. Mattel, themselves, produced this doll for Estrela, Brazil in their own China plants, yet included all of their licensee's logos. The doll speaks Portuguese and is very, very hard to come by!

Falemos Tu E Eu!
#14543 • 1995 • $125

Manufactured for Mattel/Portugal for exclusive sale in Portugal, this doll speaks a distinctive Portuguese dialect.

Parlem Tu I Jo Barbie
#12381 • 1995 • $125

Mattel had to go through much extra effort to produce Teen Talk Barbie dolls for their various European markets. Not only did they have to record Barbie doll's voice in each country's native language, but they had to manufacture a special box just for each doll and country. This one is for Mattel/Spain and speaks Spanish, of course.

Te Parle Barbie
#12372 • 1994 • $125

This version was manufactured in China (all of the Teen Talks were) for Mattel/France and of course, the doll speaks French! Teen Talks designed by Geralyn Nelson.

Barbie in India
#N/A • 1991 • $65

Leo, Mattel/India, designed this wonderful series of dolls for distribution in India. Some have found their way to specialty doll stores and doll shows here in America. They are a collector favorite. Leo uses fine silk, rayon, and lurex fabrics in many variations and colors on their dolls. This fine white jacquard sari with gold lamé trim is fantastic with Barbie doll's black hair. *Courtesy of Margo Rana.*

Barbie in India
#N/A • 1991 • $65

I recently purchased a Leo, Mattel dealer catalog, and discovered that the first Barbie in India dolls received the 1991 Doll of the Year award in India. The award there is as prestigious as the Doll of the Year Award (DOTY) sponsored by *Doll Reader®* magazine here in the U.S. Barbie doll is stunning in a buttercup-colored sari with red and gold trim. The short sleeve shell is the same color and style as the Barbie in India doll on left. *Courtesy of Margo Rana.*

Barbie in India
#N/A • 1991 • $65

Each of the dolls in this series has the current Superstar face mold. This particular doll has the unusual wave-shaped eyebrow. This spring-green silk sari has an unusually large paisley border. Of the four dolls featured in this book, this is the only one whose sari comes up over her right shoulder. *Courtesy of Margo Rana.*

Barbie in India
#N/A • 1991 • $65

Barbie in India doll's sari is wonderfully woven with fine gold, red, magenta metallic threads, creating a festive floral pattern. All of these dolls have excellent quality metal bow earrings, single jeweled necklace, ring, and multi-bangle bracelets. Each doll comes with shoes that cannot be seen because of the length of their dresses, but you can see the same style used on the dolls featured on the next page. *Courtesy of Margo Rana.*

83

Barbie in India
#9910 • circa 1990s • $75

Not as well known and a little harder to acquire, are these two dolls. Notice the difference between the capitalization of the letter "I" and "A", in the word "India". This defines the two different groupings. These collection boxes are more contemporary window boxes that come with a white cardboard sleeve which slips over the doll box as you see on the right. This doll wears a long sleeve, round neck goldenrod top, with matching straight leg pants; over which is a matching scarf and skirt of gold lurex paisley.

Barbie in India
#9910 • early 1990s • $75

The vibrant colors used by Leo for these dolls is a welcome pleasure from the pastel pink that Barbie doll is known so well for. Notice how they have taken great care on painting this doll's eyes to coordinate with her attire. This second offering is yet another winner for Leo! The brunette beauty is dressed in a pretty hot pink and bright turquoise ensemble with gold and pink accent brass jewelry. It is hard to pick a favorite when they are all so wonderful, isn't it?

My First Skipper
#9911 • 1992 • $24 each

Leo, Mattel/India offered a very basic, inexpensive Skipper doll that was available wearing very simple fashions. All of the dolls were dressed in different color knit tops that were worn over assorted colored shorts or pants. I have yet to find the doll with pigtails as the one pictured on the box. Each of the Skipper dolls has the same blonde side ponytail. The dolls have been found with both violet and blue eyes. These dolls may appear to be a little chubby. The reason for that is they all have assorted print or solid colored underwear underneath their pants. The culture in India requires that the dolls have proper undergarments on, regardless of production cost.

Japanese Traveling Sisters Gift Set

This gift set was manufactured and packaged for the Japanese market with the Bob Mackie face mold. This same set was offered in the U.S. as a customized doll for Toys 'R Us, FAO Schwarz, and JC Penney. The Barbie doll in their gift sets had the Superstar face mold. When Mattel designed this darling set, they had both face molds in mind, so the front of the box shows the closed mouth doll for the Japanese market and the open-mouth doll for the American market. Either set is a welcome treasure. *Courtesy of Margo Rana.*

Dream Rose Bride
#1861 • 1994 • $95

Mattel re-issued this bride in their Indonesian plant. The box has the new beveled edges that the U.S. one didn't. The facial paint is real subtle compared to that of the U.S.'s '92 issue that was manufactured in China. The writing on the box is Chinese.

Disney Weekend Gift Set
#0041-6661 • 1995 • $165

This Disney Weekend gift set is written in Chinese. It is a rare and unusual set created for the Asian market. This set comes in a large pink box with Mickey Mouse silhouettes. The set includes the Euro-Disney weekend doll and extra peach ballgown made from glitter fabric. Collectors searching for unique items will find this very rare gift set a super collection addition.

Barbie Style Barbie
#12292 • 1994 • $45

The Japanese market offers slim-line boxed dolls as we do here in the U.S. They are on par with our customized supermarket specials, or equivalent to our slim-box regular-line dolls. Collectors compare Barbie Style doll, shown on the left, to the American Easter Party and Easter Fun dolls.

Cha Cha Barbie
#12433 • 1995 • $45

The doll on the right may look familiar to you as it was available in the U.S as Ruffle Fun. This doll was also available in Europe. The back of the box tells a cute story about Cha-Cha dancing.

87

Butterfly Princess Barbie
#13051 • 1995 • $85

This Japanese version of Butterfly Princess is a sheer knock-out with the closed-mouth Mackie face mold, flawless facial paint, and lovely pale skin tone. The gown is identical to the one worn on the U.S. and European versions. It is very interesting that the Japanese have included a storybook in this doll's box but only in English!

Let's Take a Walk with Barbie and Kelly Gift Set
#13742 • 1995 • $75

Let's Take A Walk Barbie and Kelly is a main-line doll in Japan. Kelly, Barbie doll's little sister waves good-bye while Barbie doll pushes her stroller. *Courtesy of Judy Schizas.*

Songbird Barbie
#14320 • 1996 • $85

In 1996 Songbird Barbie doll was available in the U.S. as a regular-line doll and here she is in Japanese packaging with the Bob Mackie face mold. The photo on the box is the open-mouth Superstar mold. The Japanese boxes all included a quote on the side of the box that reads: "Barbie is the most beautiful and popular girl who is always leading the newest trends. She has a fun and fashionable lifestyle that you can really enjoy."

Pretty Hearts Barbie
#14473 • 1995 • $45

Pretty Hearts Barbie doll was released in Europe and the U.S. with the open-mouth face mold. Barbie doll's two-piece dress is simple which helps keep the price down. It is a good starter doll for those who enjoy dressing their dolls. The box shows three Fashion Avenue styles and the translation on the box encourages the customer to buy all the fashions to dress their dolls. The little red corduroy is referred to as casual mini short pants, the gold dress is called gold concert date, and the blue outfit is fashion date suit.

Otomodachi, Friend Barbie
#14476 • 1996 • $45

Otomodachi Barbie doll was designed for the Japanese market. The box is written in Japanese. This closed mouth, light-skinned doll is a Japanese favorite. The doll with the Superstar Face shown on the back of this box were available in Europe, Canada, and other countries. Otomodachi Barbie doll wears a kicky denim jumper, white knit turtleneck with red stripes on each arm, and high-top shoes and white socks. *Courtesy of Judy Schizas.*

Ribbons and Roses Gift Set
#62172 • 1995 • $150

This Ribbons and Roses Gift Set was found in Hong Kong. The Asian packaged set includes the 1995 Ribbons and Roses doll that was a Sears customized doll. The box, with its handle at the top, allows you to tote the box like a carry-case. The doll is packaged with a white bed and a floral comforter with matching pillow. This rare and unique combination makes collecting foreign product so enjoyable.

Flower Date Barbie
#62692 • 1995 • $65

Isn't she fabulous? The closed mouth Bob Mackie face mold, as I said before, is extremely popular in Japan. Barbie doll wears a retro-look yellow and pink crushed velvet dress, white knit hose, white high-top shoes and comes with a pink beret trimmed with jeweled flowers to match the ones on the dress. The Flower Date dress is the same fashion that was sold separately in a window box in the Fashion Avenue assortment. The fashion alone was a challenge to find in some parts of the United States. The theory is that many of the produced fashions were taken to dress the Japanese doll you see here; consequently the fashion alone was not easily found.

American Doll
#635151 • 1985 • $395

There were several dolls designed by the famous Japanese designer Hiromichi Nakano which comprised a fabulous series of dolls for the collection called American doll. These dolls were done by Takara under license by Mattel. This blonde reproduction Barbie doll is a flawless recreation wearing a very high-style ensemble that is one of the finest sewn quality garments ever produced for Barbie doll. American Doll wears a smart pink velvet fitted skirt, long sleeve turtleneck knit top, short pink velvet bolero jacket with a large wide black patent leather belt to cinch the waist. Covering this fabulous suit is an exquisite fully lined wool plaid swing coat which is trimmed at the collar and cuff with real black fur. This is an incredible doll of the highest caliber.

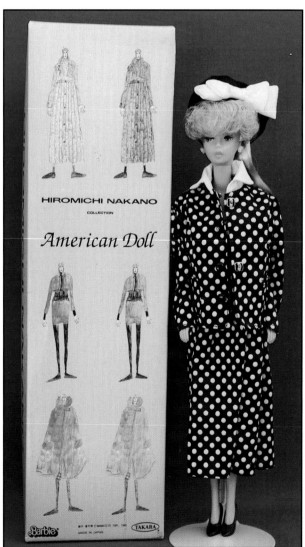

American Girl Collection
N/A • 1985 • $350

If I could only have one of these dolls, it would be a very difficult decision to choose between the two. Hiromichi Nakano used this reproduction doll to dress his smashing over-sized black and white polka-dot suit. This smart-looking couture design is trimmed with a bright white collar that matches the bow on the doll's big pouf black chapeaux.

Maba PB/Ponytail Red Dress Barbie
#DT-014 • 1986 • $300

This brunette reproduction ponytail doll is wearing a very dramatic red and black formal. Barbie doll's shoulder bow is flocked velveteen and matches the one on her hemline. The flounce at the bottom is black velvet.

Maba PB Bubble Cut Barbie
#DT-015 • 1986 • $250

During the mid to late '80s a number of reproduction dolls were produced. This particular doll is a repro bubble cut. The victorian style sienna cotton dress with white yoke and matching cuffs, is trimmed with pearls to match the one on the high collar. Barbie doll's white eyelet bloomers can be seen through the sheer organdy hemline. Sienna shoes match the dress and a tan cotton floppy hat completes the look.

Maba PB Barbie
#PB-02BL • 1986 • $250

Barbie doll wears a re-make Solo in the Spotlight fashion with a faux-fur boa and sparkly rhinestone necklace that would rival any Eisenberg. A pink cardboard box makes it easy to get the dolls out for those of us who truly enjoy displaying our dolls properly. It also allows the collector to re-package if they need to store their dolls.

Maba PB Uchikake Kimono Barbie
#PB-04 • 1986 • $300

Maba produced this reproduction brunette ponytail Barbie doll wearing a gorgeous red floral print Kimono with a white jacquard print halter. This doll's hair ornaments add to her breathtaking quality.

PB Maba PB Wedding Barbie Doll
#PB-010B • 1986 • $250

This reproduction wedding dressed Barbie doll is wearing a satin bodice, Venetian lace around the neck, cap sleeve gown with a chantilly lace skirt. The veil is styled like Barbie doll's original 1959 veil with extra long illusion and lily of the valley details added. PB Maba wedding doll carries a lily bouquet.

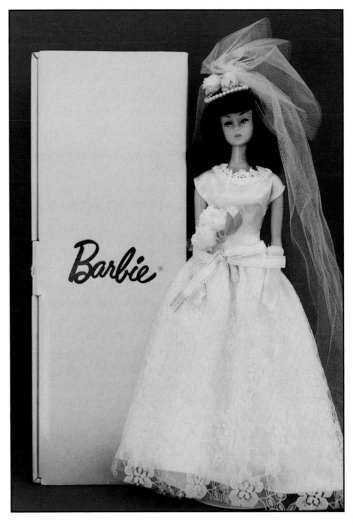

Barbie 5th Anniversario
#6294 • 1985 • $125

Mattel/Mexico celebrated their 5th Anniversary with this set. This blonde haired, brown-eyed beauty wears a simple, but elegant one shoulder dress of red chiffon with gold dots. This gift set comes with several other mix-and-match garments for endless fashion combinations.

Barbie Sensación
#8481 • 1987 • $95

Mexico produced their own dolls for a number of years. This multi-piece fashion set is similar to those produced by Rotoplast of Venezuela. Barbie doll wears a beautiful gown of blue satin with multi-colored textured satin top and comes with extra mix-and-match pieces so the collector or child can make many different looks. This set is very hard to find.

Barbie Celebración
#9146 • 1987 • $120

Barbie Celebración is another Mattel/Mexico gift set. Barbie doll's raspberry two-piece lurex knit gown, with the extra satin pieces you see still attached to the box liner, makes a fun mix-and-match wardrobe for the doll. Shoulder length blonde hair comes with a single braided wrap which acts as a hair band.

Workout Ken Aeróbico
N/A • 1989 • $55

Basa is the company in Peru that was licensed by Mattel to manufacture dolls in that South American country. We only have two Ken dolls from Basa to show you. Workout Ken doll is Basa's counter part to the Great Shapes, regular line dolls that were offered in the U.S. This doll is dressed very differently than the Ken doll that was sold here. You will notice on the back of the box that Barbie doll's workout clothes are in black, rather than the turquoise body suit and leggings that she wore in America. The workout machinery appears to be the same as ours. Ken doll's reddish-brown hair is not a common color. The spandex bike shorts with green piping accent the matching shirt, socks, and towel. Other accessories are a gym bag and black athletic shoes.

Garden Party Ken
N/A • 1990 • $75

This is Garden Party Ken doll. Garden Party Barbie doll was available in the U.S. and can be seen here on the back of the box, Ken doll was not manufactured for domestic distribution. This doll is quite handsome in a white sateen tuxedo with lavender satin shirt, bow tie, cummerbund, and corsage. A perfect compliment to Garden Party Barbie.

Career Whitney
#4118 • 1988 • $85

There were three career-dressed boxed dolls Mattel, Asia LTD manufactured for sale in the Philippines. This Whitney doll is incredible with two-tone colored hair. Whitney wears a red knit sheath underneath a print knit coat of medium blue, red, and black. In addition to this, the doll came with a powder blue ribbon in her hair, red mules, and a red scarf.

Dazzling Pretty Barbie
#4688 • 1988 • $75

Dazzling Pretty Barbie doll was made under license by Mattel, Asia LTD for the exclusive sale in the Philippines. Barbie doll wears one of the fashions that was sold separately in the United States called Perfume Pretty. She looks dazzling in it, doesn't she?

Adventure Lovin' Barbie
#6392 • 1989 • $75
Adventure Lovin' Barbie doll could have been found in a different jumpsuit. This lavender and white printed one is the rarer of the two.

Adventure Lovin' Barbie
#6392 • 1989 • $65
This jumpsuit is the same style as the one on the left. The prints are entirely different. This is the one shown on the box.

Adventure Lovin' Barbie
#6438 • 1989 • $65

This doll wears canvas olive-colored Bermuda shorts with pleats and a loose fitting short cotton blouse with polka dots. A hint of canary yellow in her hair, on her feet, and on the yellow palm tree on her shorts, adds color.

Adventure Lovin' Barbie
#6439 • 1989 • $75

Adventure Lovin' Barbie doll hopes to spot many giraffes and zebras on her safari expedition, but she might have a difficult time getting around in those yellow pumps. The darling jungle print cotton suit is pretty cute, especially with a matching yellow safari hat.

Party Fun Barbie
#6458 • 1989 • $65

Collectors flip over Richwell's short curly hair. They sure have the knack of rooting Barbie doll's hair in short styles. This doll looks great in pink and white seersucker Bermuda shorts with cuffs, and a pink polka dot blouse. The pink belt is reminiscent of Barbie doll's vintage belts.

Party Fun Barbie
#6467 • 1989 • $55

There were four Party Fun dolls in the group, unfortunately I only have three to show you. Here Barbie doll is wearing a summery chic red and white cotton stripe nautical dress with red mules. The doll's hair is worn in a simple loose ponytail. Interesting to note here is that Richwell packages all of their Barbie doll's undies in a cello package with the shoes and hairbrush.

Party Fun Barbie
#6458 • 1989 • $65

Party Fun Barbie doll is wearing a classic strapless cotton sheath dress. The floral print of pastel blue, pink, lavender, and green is trimmed in purple satin on the bodice and at the waist. It closes at the back with real snaps, not that nasty velcro. Lavender mules and a matching hair ribbon complete the ensemble.

Glamour Girl Barbie
#8917 • 1990 • $125

Richwell produced this breathtaking doll for the Philippines. Glamour Girl Barbie doll wears a form fitting pink spandex dress with pleated tulle hemline and a pink and white graduated overskirt. The accessories include lace removable sleeves, a satin drawstring purse, and pink high heels with molded bows.

Luv'n Lacy Barbie
#7363 • 1991 • $85

Luv'n Lacy Barbie would not be complete without a pastel pink dress. This doll is the only one with a peplum.

Luv'n Lacy Barbie
#7367 • 1991 • $85

The Luv'n Lacy Barbie doll collection has a lot of display versatility. They would look great around an Easter basket. The colors and fabrics are so very soft and feminine, like Barbie doll herself.

Luv'n Lacy Barbie
#7369 • 1991 • $85

Richwell designed these four lacy dolls for the Philippine market. Each one has a different hair style and although at first glance, the lace dresses look the same, they are entirely different styles. Each doll comes with hair bobs, matching lace purse, ring, earrings, and shoes. These dolls would make wonderful bridesmaids in a rainbow wedding display.

Luv'n Lacy Barbie
#7370 • 1991 • $85

This soft green lace doll with the longest ringlets is visually cool and refreshing like parfait.

Trendy Style Barbie
#8444 • 1991 • $75

Trendy Style Barbie doll is a real treat to see with strawberry blonde curly locks tied back off her face so you can see those wonderful big blue eyes. The raspberry denim full circle skirt with white net petticoat comes with a matching vest. Barbie doll's white T-shirt has a floral decal. Accessories include raspberry pumps to match and a yellow walk-man, like those that Mattel gave to the European Music Lovin' dolls from 1985.

Trendy Style Barbie
#8446 • 1991 • $65

Trendy Style Barbie doll is a trendsetter in smashing jade color biker shorts, yellow knit T-shirt with "B" logo appliqué and a smart jade jumper. The skirt ruffle is trimmed with buttercup yellow to match the shoes.

Sweet Dreams Barbie
#8459 • 1991 • $65 (White P.J.s)
#8458 • 1991 • $65 (Pink short nighty)

There were four different Sweet Dreams Barbie dolls for sale in the Philippines in 1991. Each gift set comes with a lingerie bag or pillow and nylon sleepwear trimmed with delicate lace. Very few dolls have braided pigtails. This particular group has two dolls with braids in the collection.

Fashion Fun Barbie
#0144 • 1992 • $55

For the last several years, Richwell has been export-ing Barbie dolls for sale to Australia. Many of these dolls have been found with Japanese writing. Sue Munt, a Mattel Marketing friend in Australia con-firms this to be true. Fashion Fun Barbie doll wears a simple yet elegant gold lamé bow at the shoulder and a removable gold ruffle at the waistline. The doll's hair is an unusual two-tone shade of golden blonde worn in a simple topknot.

Summer Cool Barbie
#6849 • 1992 • $45

Summer Cool Barbie doll will stay cool on any beach in a two-piece swimsuit made from jersey knit. This outfit is reminiscent of the first Midge doll swimsuits.

Fancy Ribbon Barbie
#6852 • 1992 • $65

There are four Fancy Ribbon Barbie dolls in this series. All have nautical print attire. This particular one is wearing a cotton sport crop-top with a large plastic bow accent from which the series gets it's name. The skirt is short and sporty. The only accessories that come with this doll are pearl button earrings and red mule shoes.

Sweetheart Barbie
#7357 • 1992 • $125

There were two styles of Sweetheart Barbie dolls available in 1992. The bottom right doll came packaged in an acrylic box with Barbie embossed on the bottom and top lid. The first releases were packaged in a pink and yellow box as you see on the bottom left.

Dream Girl Barbie
#07362 • 1992 • $125

Richwell created two different dolls in this series. I only have one to show you. This one comes in a Lucite box with "Barbie" embossed on the plastic lid and bottom. Dream Girl Barbie doll wears a gorgeous gown with a gold lamé bodice and layers of gold and white etched lace. There's a matching gold lamé rose in the doll's hair. Accessories include: earrings, necklace, shoes, and gold clutch purse.

Sara Lee Barbie
#60403 • 1993 • $65

Sara Lee Barbie doll was made by Richwell and was sold at Sara Lee, a clothing store chain in the Philippines (don't be confused with the Sara Lee Bakery company here in the U.S.). Barbie doll wears a sporty short set with pink and white candy cane shorts trimmed in lavender to match the lavender nylon top with the Sara Lee logo on the front. Accessories include: a coordinating headband, sneakers, and bracelets.

Dancin' Rap Barbie
#7358 • 1994 • $65

Dancin' Rap Barbie doll is an absolute gorgeous strawberry blonde with mounds of curls, exquisite facial paint, and wonderful lavender eyes. The doll is ready to step onto the dance floor in a pink washed denim dress, trimmed in pink lamé with brass studs. The net scarf around her neck matches the hat adorned with a pink heart.

Private Collection Barbie
#2715 • 1994 • $150

Richwell of the Philippines manufactured dressed-boxed dolls. The fashions that these dolls wore were called Private Collection Fashions in the U.S., while in Europe they were called Haute Couture. The doll on this page is wearing the Haute Couture, fashion #2715, that was only sold in Europe. There was a difference between this dressed box doll and the single fashion. The doll wears a yellow satin top and the Euro *haute couture* fashion is a genuine raw silk textured, pattern yellow shell. The package is a Plexiglas style box with the name Barbie embossed on the hard plastic top as well as on the bottom.

Chic and Sassy Barbie
#61366 • 1994 • $65

Chic and Sassy Barbie doll is bright and cheerful in a daffodil yellow knit halter dress with a slit midi length hemline. Barbie doll's accessories include headband, earrings, purse with pearl-chain strap, and pumps of the same bright daffodil yellow.

Chic and Sassy Barbie
#61364 • 1994 • $65

At first glance, you might think that this Chic and Sassy doll is wearing the same style dress as her friend, but if you look again, you will see that they are slightly different. This doll's marine blue casual knit dress has shoulder straps and no slit in the front. Both dolls share similar accessories, and have their own gray kitty.

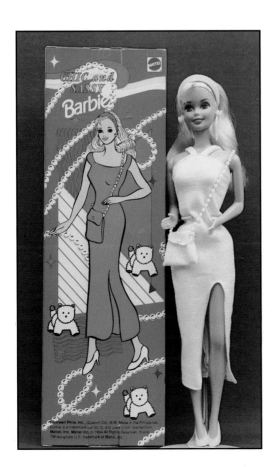

Hot 'n Trendy Barbie
#61361 • 1994 • $65

This fabulous blonde gal is ready for a day of shopping in a white and red polka dot short flared skirt with coordinating striped crop-top with dot trim to match the skirt. Accessories include a raspberry colored felt brimmed hat, matching drawstring purse, large fun earrings, and white pumps.

Hot 'n Trendy Barbie
#61362 • 1994 • $75

Barbie doll is off to see all the sights the Islands have to offer in this marine blue knit skirt with quite a slit in front. The doll's blue and white halter top is cinched at the waist with a wide, white belt. Accessories include a big brimmed hat, shoulder bag, earrings, and blue pumps.

Hot 'n Trendy Barbie
#61363 • 1994 • $75

Hot 'n Trendy Barbie doll makes and sets trends with a high quality Caribbean style raspberry knit skirt and polka dot one shoulder top. Accessories include a matching polka dot drawstring shoulder bag, big white brimmed hat, a white belt, earrings, and hot pink pumps.

Miss Barbie
#61747 • 1994 • $55

Miss Barbie doll has been found in Australia in Coles Supermarkets, and randomly throughout Japan. The doll's attire is similar to other back-to-school exclusive dolls produced in the United States.

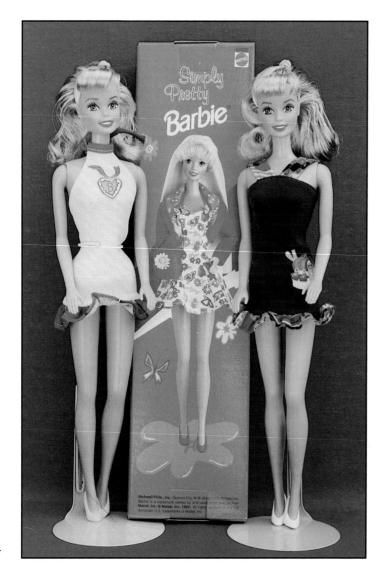

Simply Pretty Barbie
#62020 • 1995 • $45

Simply Pretty Barbie doll comes packaged one way, but the dolls have different colored outfits. Their dresses are made of spandex and are trimmed with multi-color printed canvas.

Beauty Barbie
#62091 • 1995 • $95

This is one of Richwell's newest releases. The gown is layers of pink tulle and silver lace, with a silver and white bodice. There are pretty lace accents adorning the doll's shoulders. The packaging is original. The front of the box gives the illusion that there are stage doors that open and there Barbie doll is waiting to make a grand entrance.

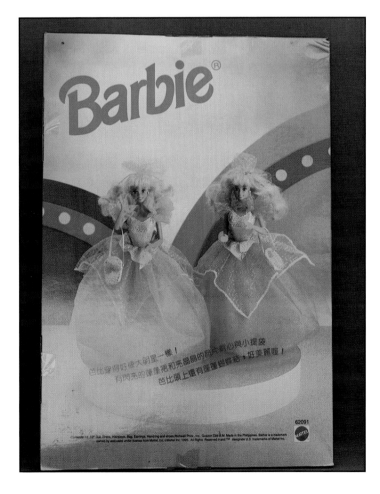

Gymnast Barbie
#62150 • 1995 • $65

Richwell produced three gymnast dolls. There is one version, not shown, that is almost identical to the U.S.'s 1994 gymnast. This series includes two additional versions for the Philippine market only. The first one wears a dark pink spandex ballet dress with light pink glittery tulle ruffles and sleeves with matching pink ballet slippers. The doll has gorgeous violet eyes, deep tanned skin, and a ribbon braided ponytail.

Gymnast Barbie
#62149 • 1995 • $65

The second exclusive Richwell Gymnast doll shown here is outfitted with a purple stretch knit tutu with lavender ruffled lace hem and armlets, purple ribbon braided ponytail, lavender ballet slippers, and a dark purple canvas tote bag.

Jollibee Barbie
#62126 • 1995 • $55

The dolls you see on the next two pages were manufactured for exclusive sale in a fast food chain restaurant throughout the Philippines. They are seldom found at U.S. doll shows. The artwork on the side of the boxes shows a boxed pie like those sold at McDonald's. The pie featured on the box is peach mango, sounds delicious. Barbie doll is wearing a cool summer frock made of navy nylon and trimmed with white lace.

Jollibee Barbie
#62125 • 1995 • $55

Of the four dolls, this is the only brown-eyed brunette. Jollibee Barbie doll is wearing a chartreuse and bold blue exercise suit that resembles the U.S.'s Wet and Wild collection.

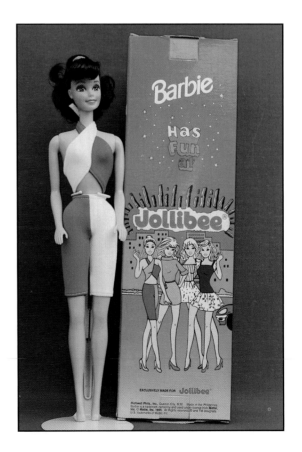

Jollibee Barbie
#62123 • 1995 • $55

This Jollibee Barbie doll is wearing a long sleeve turtle-neck top with an elastic pull-on denim skirt.

Jollibee Barbie
#62124 • 1995 • $55

The fourth Jollibee Barbie doll's blonde two-tone hair is streaked which sets this doll apart from the others. This little red and white candy striped top with matching skirt is wonderful for a hot summer day.

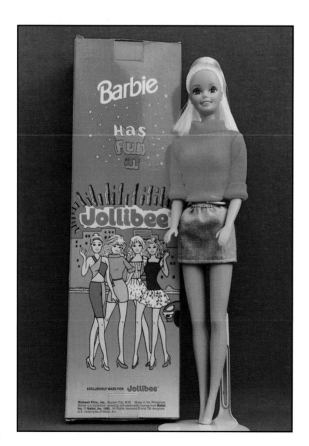

Stylish Barbie
#62332 • 1995 • $50

There are three Stylish Barbie dolls in this series by Richwell. Each wears a different style with the same wonderful paisley print. I only have this one to show you but this doll is so stylish we know you'll get the idea.

Hair Style Barbie
#62543 • 1995 • $55

Hair Style Barbie doll is very unusual indeed in a sharp-looking magenta and silver lamé dress with pink pumps. The box states "style her hair and magically make it grow longer". It even pictures the doll with longer braided hair, with one doll's hair to the floor. However, there is not a grow-hair mechanism on this doll and she did not come with hair pieces, so it is impossible to achieve these looks. Included with the doll are rollers and a shower cap.

Beachtime Barbie
#15126 • 1996 • $40

Beachtime Barbie doll is one of Richwell's newer releases. The doll wears a perky 2-piece floral print skort with matching halter top. A **skort** is a pair of shorts that is so full that they look like a skirt. You can see two other versions of Beachtime on the box.

Nostalgic Barbie
#62328 • 1996 • $75

In 1996 Richwell produced three Barbie dolls in the Philippines under the Nostalgic Barbie logo. All three dolls were made with the Superstar head mold and wear up-dated versions of the 1960s classic Solo in the Spotlight fashion. The script used on the package is the same as that used on the U.S. nostalgic series. These dolls are a different and contemporary way of saluting Barbie doll's past. Can't wait to see what they have in store for the future!

Nostalgic Barbie
#62327 • 1996 • $75

This Solo in the Spotlight doll is most like the original and the U.S. reproduction Nostalgic doll. From topknot to hemline, necklace to flounce, the doll is virtually identical. A net shawl has been added, the necklace changed from clear to gold, and the pink scarf has been eliminated.

Nostalgic Barbie
#62329 • 1996 • $75

Of the three dolls in this collection, this is the one that is most watered-down from the original Solo in the Spotlight fashion. The flounce as seen on the other two has been removed completely.

Party Time Barbie
#62713 • 1996 • $45

It's party time! And Barbie doll is ready to have a fun time in red knit slacks. An off the shoulder red, green, purple, and yellow print top with ruffle collar match the sash on the pants.

Party Time Barbie
#62713 • 1996 • $55

The Richwell Company uses some of the nicest fabrics and takes great care in the construction of clothing. All of the dolls have wonderful facial paint. It is particularly evident in this photograph of Party Time Barbie doll. The two piece jewel tone raspberry and white striped day dress is adorable. This is one of several new releases in 1996.

Day-to-Night/Dia-y-Noche Barbie
 # N/A • mid 1980s • $95

Day-to-Night Barbie doll may look familiar to you, because this doll was also released by Mattel in Europe and the U.S. The doll had the same clothing with identical fabric and colors as the other versions. This doll is featured so that you can see the exceptional face-painting workmanship of Rotoplast. *Courtesy of Carolyn Klemovec.*

Barbie and The Rockers
#N/A • 1986 • $165

Whether they are from America, Venezuela, or Argentina, Barbie and The Rockers are the hottest rock band! How wonderful can the girl get? This fashion is as sparkly as her eyes. The black knit jacket and raspberry leggings are threaded with mylar that glitters under the lights. The top is silver lamé, and the skirt and shoe toppers are white leatherette. Accessories are earrings, ring, shoes, and microphone (not shown). *Courtesy of Margo Rana.*

Barbie and The Rockers, Diva
#N/A • 1986 • $150

Rotoplast created this version of Diva for sale in Venezuela. The dolls on the back of the box are the same dolls and fashions that were available in the U.S. Diva doll's stage attire is definitely different from Mattel/USA's release. Diva doll wears a raspberry and blue metallic stretch knit ensemble with a bright yellow lace halter top. The accessories were the same as Barbie doll's, but with one addition, Diva has a bracelet. *Courtesy of Margo Rana.*

Barbie and The Rockers, Derek
#N/A • 1986 • $75

Ken doll was not included in this collection. Derek doll, who looks more South American, is the lead male singer. The three Rocker dolls shown are all wearing different attire and have different face paint than the Mattel produced dolls for the American and international markets. For their South American tour, Derek opts for a gold lamé jacket with pink satin trim and matching cummerbund, rather than the printed one on the box. *Courtesy of Margo Rana.*

Springtime Primavera Barbie
NONE • late 1980s • $225

Springtime Primavera is one of the prettiest dolls, former Mattel licensee, Rotoplast, ever produced for the Venezuelan market. Barbie doll's bright white sheer chiffon gown is a wonderful gown to wear while walking through the park with her best beau, Ken. The illusion parasol is perfect to keep the sun from damaging her fair skin. This doll has exceptional face paint and her ash blonde hair is gorgeous!

Emerald Esmeralda Doll
N/A • late 1980s • $150

This illustrious beauty hails from Venezuela and was made under license from Mattel, Inc. by the innovative Rotoplast Corporation. Rotoplast created some of the most beautiful fashions. Esmeralda doll wears a brilliant emerald green layered chiffon gown with a ruffled wrap and a rose corsage pinned at the bodice. An emerald colored choker adorns her neck and accents her eyes. *Courtesy of Margo Rana.*

Blue Magic Barbie
N/A • late 1980s • $150

Blue Magic Barbie doll in a turquoise blue knit jersey is sumptuous. Over the one shoulder, one sleeved, body suit is a superb lace skirt with faux fur trim to match the muff the doll carries on her bare-shoulder arm. There are three simple pearls sewn at the shoulder just below the one gold earring which matches the gold ring on her finger.

Crystal Barbie
#4598 • circa late 1980s • $150

Crystal Barbie doll appears to be just like the U.S. issue. This is the one that Rotoplast made in Venezuela. With a full head of hair, intense face paint and sultry eyes, this doll is a must-have for the serious collector. This is an all-time favorite from the '80s.

Alta Costura Fashion

It is no secret that some of the best fashions of the last several decades were produced by Mattel for exclusive sale in Europe only! They are of high quality fabrics and workmanship. Collectors strive to obtain these fashions from collectors throughout the world. This is the back of the fashion boxes.

Alta Costura Fashion
#7202 • 1984 • $75

This one is packaged for Mattel/Spain, but the ensemble was released in other European countries under the Haute Couture labeling. The fashion is a classic style gown of emerald satin with a lace trim hemline. A short matching bolero jacket with lace trim and white mules complete the ensemble.

Alta Costura Fashion
#7204 • 1984 • $75

Another fashion from Mattel/Spain. This fashion was also released in the rest of Europe under the Haute Couture label. This fashion resembles the dress Julie Andrews wore in Disney's infamous *Mary Poppins* carousel scene!

Haute Couture Fashions

#9151 • 1984 • $75

A rich ensemble of autumn hues, this wonderful set consists of a rust blouse, slacks, black velvet skirt, and multi-colored abstract print velvet jacket. Accessories include a coordinating hat and black pumps.

#9149 • 1984 • $75

This is an extremely rare and most difficult to find fashion. This particular fashion consists of a gold, mauve and purple metallic long skirt with a glittered hemline. A pink long sleeved lamé top with satin bow is worn with this evening skirt. Mauve colored pumps are the choice of shoes here.

#5843 • 1982 • $75

This rich ensemble consists of a blue wool midi-skirt and matching top with large cowl neck collar, coordinating wool trousers, gold belt, plum-colored pantyhose and scarf, black leather purse, and blue mules.

#5845 • 1982 • $75

This fashion was purchased at the famous Hamley's of London toy store with the price tag in pounds still intact. This exceptional quality fashion set consists of brown leather-look riding pants, brown and off-white houndstooth jacket, matching scarf, turtleneck blouse, leather-look shoulder bag, and brown riding boots.

Haute Couture Fashions

#5842 • 1982 • $85

A mix-and-match ensemble of a brown satin skirt with rust waistband and ecru lace blouse, rust jacket, and rust bolero pants. Hard to find! This one was purchased from Harrods of London and still has the price on the top of the box.

#4873 • 1983 • $85

Mattel changed the color, kept the pattern identical and issued a new stock number to include this version for the following year. This fashion featured a black satin skirt, red suede cummerbund, white lace blouse, red suede jacket, and red suede bolero slacks. Hard to find.

#7201 • 1983 • $75

This fashion consists of a grey and blue tweed skirt, slacks, shawl, and wool top with beret.

#9150 • 1984 • $75

A smart dress consisting of a black skirt with a red and black striped bodice. The dress has a large bow at the neckline and is worn underneath a great black and grey herringbone coat with "fur" trim and cuffs. Accessories include: a matching fur hat, black pantyhose, black shoulder bag, and black pumps.

Haute Couture Fashions

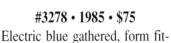

#9148 • 1984 • $85
A real smart ensemble of burgundy slacks, mauve top, burgundy and mauve striped wool jacket with grey fur trim, grey shoulder bag, and grey pumps!

#3278 • 1985 • $75
Electric blue gathered, form fitting satin gown with a gorgeous metallic jacket of gold and electric blue print. Includes head ornament, purse, and pumps.

#3265 • 1986 • $75
A knockout ball gown of seafoam and raspberry satin with black lace over netting, black net hat, purse, and pumps. WOW!

#3248 • 1986 • $75
Red velvet evening gown with metallic print red and gold jacket, clutch, hat, and pumps!

INTERNATIONAL FASHIONS

Haute Couture Fashions
#3247 • 1986 • $75

A unique fashion statement! Pink and grey balloon slacks, grey metallic print jacket with a triangle print, big pouf hat, purse, and heels!

The doll modeling the outfit is wearing a proto-type (on loan from a retired Mattel Intl' division employee) where the fabric is high quality brocade and satin before Mattel copied the print to a less expensive version for mass marketing. The proto-type wearing this particular ensemble is shown on the back of the box. The 2nd doll in purple is wearing a ruffled gown made exclusively for JC Penney for their 1988 Christmas catalog. Penney's had a set of four evening gowns that many collectors overlooked. This one utilizes leftover fabric from the Haute Couture #3247 for the bodice of this elegant gown.

Alta Costura Fashions

In 1987 Mattel released six fashions in the U.S. under the "City Style" name. Two of these fashions appeared in different color fabrics for Mattel/Spain under the name of Alta Costura. These fashions are extremely rare and almost never found.

#4430 • 1987 • $75 each
(Same stock # as U.S. version but in different color and fabric)
An abstract print of purple shades make up the dress and a shawl collar, loose fitting purple acrylic jacket, hat, and purse finish the ensemble. See below.

The U.S. fashion released as one of the "City Style" ensembles in different fabric. See above.

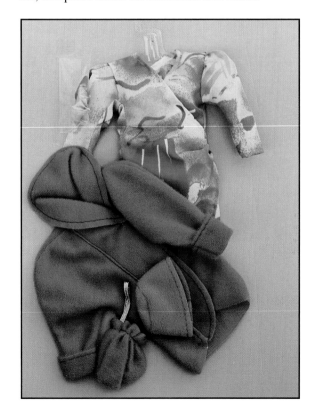

Alta Costura Fashions
#4429 • 1987 • $75 each
(also same sock # as U.S. version but in different color & fabric)

A classic black and white houndstooth skirt worn with a shell of blue, red, black, and green print and a red tailored 3/4 length jacket with purse and hat.

On the lower photos are the U.S. versions of this ensemble. The U.S. "City Style" packaging is also pictured.

Europe Alta Costura Fashion

U.S. City Style version.

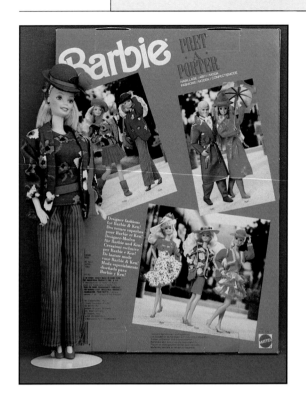

Pret-A-Porter Fashions
#7585 • 1988 • $85

In 1988 Mattel produced six fashions for the U.S. under the name "Paris Pretty" asst. stock #7590. These fashions were released in Europe under the Pret-A-Porter logo. Mattel European catalogs held a great surprise — a seventh fashion manufactured for sale exclusively in Europe! This fashion was stock #7585 and took almost two years for me to acquire because it was sold in only a few countries! I've dressed a Barbie doll in it so you can see the fashion in more depth. Raspberry and royal striped slacks are paired with a royal, raspberry, yellow and green floral knit tunic and matching knit jacket. Accessories include: a raspberry suede shoulder bag and marvelous blue felt hat with yellow and pink chiffon rose accents. On the box you'll notice the fashion looks somewhat different. Mattel used the proto-type of this fashion for the photo session. Extremely rare.

Riding Set/Ensemble Equitations
#5400 • 1987 • $65

A complete riding set for the European market only. The 1988 Toys 'R Us customized Barbie doll, released a year after the fashion, was very similar. The European fashion had differences. The jacket was red corduroy (Toys 'R Us was red "velvet") the skirt and the horse blanket were brushed acrylic (the Toys 'R Us was woven knit), the European set also included extras like a dress hat with veil and a red, white and blue ribbon for the horse's tail.

Superstyle Fashion
#2963 • 1988 • $20

Europe's version of "Style Magic" Barbie doll wears denim. There are four separate denim themed fashions that coordinate with the "Super Style" denim theme Barbie doll also sold in Europe. These fashions were hard to find and expensive in Europe. The doll can be seen on page 69.

Haute Couture Fashions
#4047 • 1991 • $65

In 1991 Mattel created "Fashion Mall" fashions in a unique package to give the appearance of a store front window! Three of the four were released in the U.S. The fourth one, "United Colors of Benetton" Boutique #4047 was marketed only in Europe. It consists of several Benetton sportswear pieces, accessories, and a Benetton shopping bag. This fashion is extremely hard to find.

Pret-A-Porter Fashions
#3307 • 1987 • $55

In 1987 Mattel produced six new Barbie doll fashions released as "Beverly Hills Fashions" in the U.S. under stock #3315. In Europe these fashions were released under the European name "Pret-A-Porter" and were marketed in a unique carry handle package. The surprise here was also the addition of two Ken doll fashions exclusive to Europe and Canada. They were hard to find and we are lucky to show you #3307 consisting of a white linen suit, marina blue knit sleeveless top, and shoes. Very rare.

Haute Couture Fashions
#2715 • 1991 • $65

In 1991 Mattel produced six new fashions of this high end quality series. Five of these were released in the U.S. under the packaging name "Private Collection". The sixth one (seen here) was only sold in the European market along with the five others under the European "Haute Couture" packaging label. This fashion, consisting of a purple culotte "velour" skirt with gold textured waistband, short gold and red brocade bolero jacket, purple print shawl, velvet paisley skirt with red fringe and red suede shoulder bag, suede boots, pumps, genuine raw silk yellow print shell and a stunning big brim red velvet hat with gold trim, is one of the finest and most detailed outfits ever.

Winter Bride Fashion
Assortment #9077 • 1990 • $75

Very rare! Winter Bride Fashion was only sold in some European countries. There are four bridal gowns in the collection; but sadly, I only have three to show you. There was also a bridesmaid and one groom Ken doll fashion. All of these fashions were designed by Carol Spencer. They were never sold or packaged on dolls as had previously been reported. This fashion is made of many pieces which enhances the play value! A white crystallized tunic dress, matching long skirt, fur trim veil and fur wrap will make a most memorable winter wedding for Barbie doll.

Summer Bride Fashion
#4896 • 1990 • $75

For a summer wedding day, Barbie doll selected this two-piece gown with ruffled armlets, veil, garter, and bouquet.

Bridesmaid Fashion
#4922 • 1990 • $75

Barbie doll's best friend will wear this lovely fashionable fuschia and lace cocktail dress with a lace crop jacket, bow, and bouquet to the wedding.

Groom Ken Fashion
#4913 • 1990 • $85

Ken doll will look splendid when he waits at the altar for Barbie doll dressed in her Winter Bride fashion. Ken doll is dashing in a glittery tuxedo of white satin with hot-pink accents. Special thanks to Barbie doll collector, Barbara Hunt for finding this elusive Ken doll fashion for me.

Couturier Fashions
#7214/#7221 • 1991 • $55 each

In 1991 Mattel produced six fashions under the "Couturier" label. Four of these six were released in the U.S. under the label packaging "Private Collection". The two European exclusives were offered in the U.S. only through JC Penney's 1991 Christmas catalog. These two fashions were packaged in a white shipping box with the Barbie logo on the back and the JC Penney catalog stock number. They were so over-looked that they are included in this book. The fashions, #7214 and #7221, are a southwestern inspired ensemble (lower left) and a gold and silver dress ensemble with white felt hat (shown at right).

Prêt-A-Porter Fashions
1991 • $45 each
Mattel introduced six new sportswear ensembles for this popular European series. The ones shown here were all found in Toronto, Canada.

#2961
Purple acrylic coat with black metallic print scarf, beret, gloves, and pumps.

#2962
Red, blue, yellow, and green floral canvas hooded parka, tights, yellow ribbed knit skirt, blue knit shell, and blue sneakers.

#2965
Wild floral vinyl raincoat, belt, large matching umbrella, scarf, and high purple rain boots.

Pret-A-Porter Fashions

1991 • $45 each

Mattel introduced six new sportswear ensembles for this popular European series. The ones shown here were all found in Toronto, Canada.

#2960

Purple "ultra-suede" mini-skirt, boots, handbag, and high quality multi-colored knit turtleneck sweater.

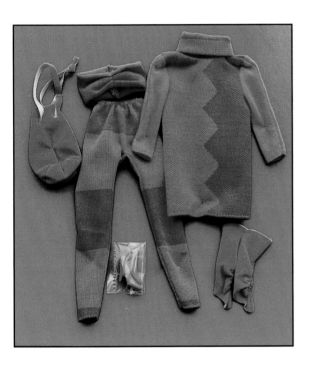

#2963

A raspberry and orange knit turtleneck dress, matching knit slacks, tube top, boots, shoes, and purse.

#2964

Purple crushed velvet hooded jumpsuit, yellow "ultra-suede" swing coat, boots, pumps, and silver and purple metallic print scarf. Incidentally, the scarf material was also used on one of the three exclusive ball gowns Mattel made for the Sears Christmas catalog.

Benetton Shopping Fashions
1991 • $45 each

Mattel went with Benetton again in 1991 but only Barbie doll of the "Shopping" series was offered in the U.S. The other four dolls and four fashions were only available in Europe.

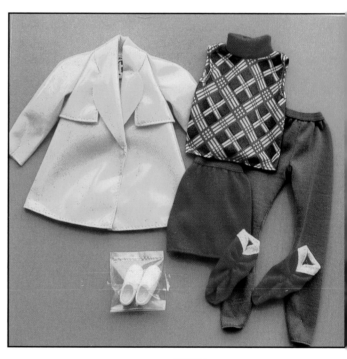

#5962
Yellow vinyl coat, red knit mini-skirt, purple tights, purple and red geometric tunic top, leg warmers, and sneakers.

#5953
Orange acrylic jacket, aqua knit jumpsuit, orange and yellow striped, hooded top, leg warmers, and sneakers.

Benetton Shopping Fashions
1991 • $45 each

Mattel went with Benetton again in 1991 but only Barbie doll of the "Shopping" series was offered in the U.S. The other four dolls and four fashions were only available in Europe.

#9487

A repeat for Ken doll. Guess Mattel had lots of remaining stock of the previous years regular U.S. Benetton line. The fashion was re-packaged and included a smart looking racing suit, T-shirt, socks, and sneakers.

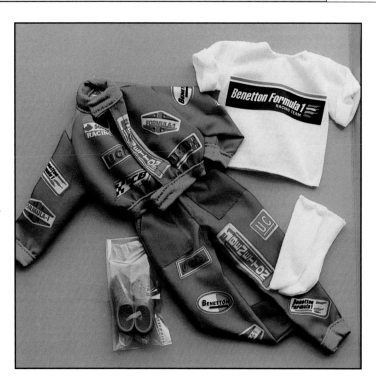

#5964

Purple, aqua and pink abstract print knit jumpsuit with yellow knit bodice, purple "suede" swing coat, sneakers, and yellow tennis shoes.

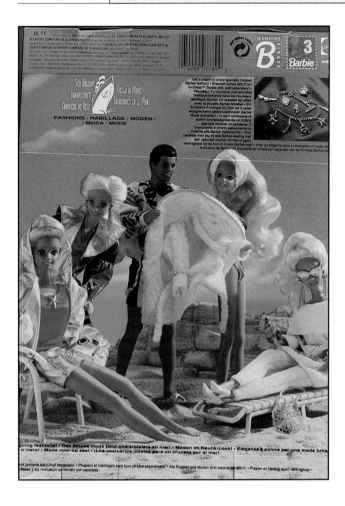

Sea Holiday Fashions
1992 • $45 each

These very hard to find fashions were only available in Europe. The Barbie, Ken, and Midge Sea Holiday dolls were also a European exclusive but Mattel offered them to specialty shops in the U.S.

#7790

Fancy white jacquard terry wrap robe with gold braid trim, two piece yacht theme satin bikini, white terry hairband, pumps, and gold sunglasses.

#7789

A beautiful gold iridescent stripe hooded cover-up, hot pink tank top, gold textured shorts, pumps, and gold sunglasses.

Sea Holiday Fashions

#7796

Blue and white cabana striped knit slacks, marina blue nautical short cropped jacket with gold collar, red tank top, pumps, and gold sunglasses.

#7797

A sharp off-white ribbed knit pantsuit with a cowl neck collar, pumps, and gold shades. *Courtesy of Margo Rana.*

#7793

The only Ken fashion of the group. Nautical print hooded jacket with gold and white braided drawstring at waist. Yellow and blue spandex trunks, tank top, sandals, and gold shades. A real neat outfit!

Pret-A-Porter Fashions
1992 • $55 each

The new European catalog showed four brand-new ensembles and two repeats from the 1991 line. The packaging was all new. I will show only four as the floral raincoat and the red floral jacket fashions are identical to the 1991 group.

#3706

Purple suede coat with black and purple animal print collar and cuffs, matching headband, pumps, and yellow and gold print scarf.

Pret-A-Porter Fashions

1992 • $55 each

The new European catalog showed four brand-new ensembles and two repeats from the 1991 line. The packaging was all new. I will show only four as the floral raincoat and the red floral jacket fashions are identical to the 1991 group.

#3707

Raspberry knit slacks, purple, yellow and raspberry knit top, unusual pom-pom hat, pumps, and boots.

#3725

The hard one of the bunch to find. Pink ribbed jacket with fur trim and collar, pastel print acrylic skirt, matching scarf, and ice skates. *$65*

#3723

Green and black tweed tailored slacks, yellow ribbed turtleneck, metallic plaid shawl, purse, and fur hat.

Crystal Fashions/Habillage
1992 • $35 each

#2181

One of four evening gowns produced for the mainline 1992 Secret Hearts and Crystal Barbie doll in Europe. These four fashions were sold only in Europe. This one is a really pretty soft peach and yellow netted and iridescent peach gown with peach pumps.

#2182

Yellow netted gown over iridescent yellow skirt, yellow ruffled neckline, and yellow pumps.

The other two fashions were not available for photographing.

Fancy Frills Lingerie/ Moda Lingerie

Assortment #10762 • 1993 • $35

Mattel designer Geralyn Nelson designed these four exquisite lingerie sets for European release only. *Courtesy of Margo Rana.*

#10759

A delightful teddy of red calico fabric, white eyelet trim, Swiss dot sheer inset, panty hose, and nylon net slip. The fabric of the teddy was also used on the Ames customized Barbie doll of 1992 called, Country Looks.

#10761

Here's a beautiful turquoise peignoir set with pink ribbon accents and lots of accessories for Barbie doll's vanity.

#10760

Barbie doll models a floral pattern and sheep pink one-piece slip with undies built into the slip. The floral fabric of the bodice was used on one of the '92 Europe Barbie Style dolls.

#10758

Barbie doll wears a very striking set of black and hot pink checkered dance pants, bra, sleeveless cover-up, and black hose.

Pret-A-Porter Fashions
Assortment Stock #10767 • 1993 • $55 each

#10763

Leopard print acrylic skirt, black fitted top with leopard print collar, gold buttons on an over-sized camel swing coat, brown spikes, purse, and black hat.

#10764

Raspberry and green plaid tailored slacks, jacket, wrap, hat, walking cane, and pumps.

Pret-A-Porter Fashions
#10765

Black textured vinyl mini-skirt, gold, aqua and brown tones polished satin jacket with black textured vinyl collar, black tights, hat, umbrella, and high blue boots.

#10765

Black and white zebra print maxi-coat with black "lamb" fur trim, red purse, scarf, hat, and black lace-up boots.

Party Moden Collection
1996 • $45 each

#12175
Black and white satin striped cocktail dress with red felt bodice, black net hose, and armlets. The choker has the same jewel buttons as used on the 1996 Happy Holidays Barbie doll.

Party Moden Collection

#12174

A halter lace cocktail dress of jewel tone colors, large pink satin bow, armlets, hose, and bag.

#12176

A luscious emerald green suit with fluted pleated collar, fluted green sleeves, green hose and matching purse.

#12177

A purple and gold lace cocktail dress worn with a loose fitting gold jacket with purple satin collar and matching purse.

Haute Couture Fashions
1992/1993 • $65 each
#2720 Six Fashion Assortments

#3844

A fashion reminiscent to JC Penney's customized Enchanted Evening doll from 1991. This one consists of a red satin fitted gown with gold lamé belt. The gorgeous purple, gold, and red brocade fabric coat is trimmed in royal blue fur. A matching hat is included.

#3843

Gold textured jacket, pink top, skirt, black "leather" slacks, and terrific black velvet brim hat. Two looks in one!

#3854

A metallic lace, layered skirt, gold lamé halter, blue suede cropped jacket with hat and purse.

#3846

Electric blue metallic skirt, yellow halter top, pink satin pleated slacks, bold print satin jacket, yellow suede boots, purse, and pink and lime trimmed brim hat.

#3847

A terrific combo here. Red tartan plaid pleated skirt, sleeveless top, purple velvet jacket trimmed with metallic braid trim, red velvet shoulder bag, tartan plaid beret. Red pumps and suede boots included for two different looks.

#3848

An unusual and bold print fabric that turns out a winning ball gown. A black velvet bodice with a splashy emblem accent the gown. A purple and gold lace wrap, gold lamé armlets and black cocktail purse are included!

Haute Couture Fashions
1994 • $45 each

Two of these four fashions were used by Mattel for their now famous "Barbie Festival" held in 1994 in Orlando, Florida to celebrate Barbie doll's 35th Anniversary. Mattel dressed two dolls in #12168 Rainbow and #12167 Red Velvet. These were boxed and sold at the Festival's limited edition sale!

#12168
Rainbow colored satin gown with short crop jacket, purse, and heels.

Haute Couture Fashions

#12176

Red velvet, fitted gown with metallic tartan plaid blouse, wrap, and short gold lamé jacket.

#12165

White chiffon gown with black polka dots and black lace bodice and sleeves, purse and heels.

#12166

Purple satin gown with purple and seafoam green metallic bodice, purse, and shoes.

167

Pret-A-Porter Fashions
Assortment Stock #12164 • 1994 • $55 each

#12164
A purple, blue and green paisley knit double breast-ed maxi-coat with blue suede collar and cuffs. Accents of six silver pearl buttons and a big brimmed velvet hat and those wonderful re-issued black lace-up boots complete the ensemble.

Pret-A-Porter Fashions
#12160

A southwestern inspired ensemble! Hot pink, yellow, brown, seafoam and orange striped loose fitting coat with black slacks, pink scarf, gloves, black "reptile" shoulder bag, pink hat, and black ankle boots.

#12161 • $65

The most difficult of the four ensembles to find. An aqua ribbed knit body suit, aqua gloves, and headband with delightful "rabbit" look parka, and pearl white ankle boots.

#12162

Red vinyl midi-trench coat with brass button accents, black and white tweed print scarf, umbrella, black felt beret, and black lace-up boots. Barbie doll is ready for a day of sightseeing in London!

Pretty Choices Gift Set
#13819 • $95 set

This is a very rare three outfit package that was sold in very select international markets! The set includes one Pret-A-Porter (#12164), one Party Modes (#12176), and one European Fancy Frills Lingerie Set (#12174).

Fashion Avenue Fashions
1996 • $35 each

These are two fashion avenue styles Mattel created exclusively for the European market in 1996. These fashions were in the U.S. Mattel Catalog but for international sale only. Rumors are that they will be out here!

#14674

Black suede shorts, white blouse, denim vest, boots, pumps, and suede purse.

14302

Denim jeans, a fabulous knit turtleneck sweater, red hiking boots, and gloves.

Mattel 1995 Japanese Dealer Catalog

This was a very hard-to-obtain catalog for Japanese retail stores and dealers. Interestingly, the Butterfly Princess shown on the cover is the one manufactured for Mattel USA/Europe. Japan, in fact, has the doll with the closed-mouth Mackie face mold and a white skin tone as you see in this book.

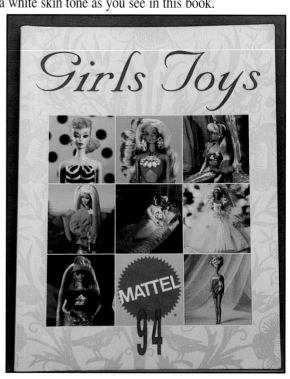

Mattel/England, 1994 Dealer Catalog

Mattel's United Kingdom catalog features the highly sought-after Magical Hair Mermaid doll. This doll was dressed in purple and has purple hair. This Barbie doll is highly sought after by collectors in the U.S.

Fun with Leo/Mattel Dealer Catalog

This is a very rare dealer catalog from India. In the Barbie section of the catalog, those great Indian Native dress Barbie dolls that you saw on pages 82-84, are shown.

1991 Dealer Catalog

This particular dealer catalog is in German and was printed for Mattel/Germany.

Paul — Sindy's New Friend
#8070 • 1987 • $85

In 1987 Hasbro introduced their version of Paul to their Sindy line. Their box descriptions say simply "Paul, Sindy's new friend is as fashion conscious as she is." Hasbro's head mold for Paul in the early years was more boyish and child-like than the present head mold. Paul's clothing is exceptional on this doll. He is wearing grey pleated corduroy trousers, white knit turtle-neck shirt, red suede bomber jacket and a great navy, red and gold plaid scarf with fringed edges.

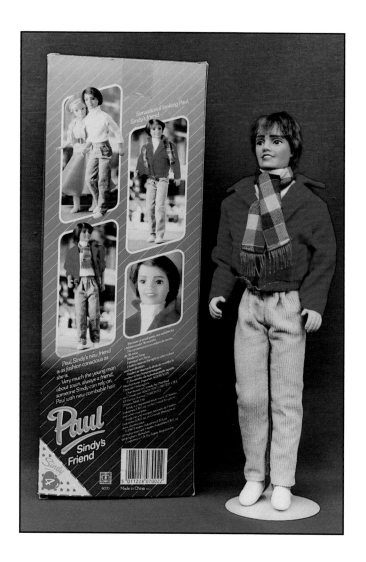

Diamond Princess Sindy
#8014 • 1990 • $85

This is one of Hasbro International's first attempts at gearing to the collector market. The doll box actually is marked "Limited Edition" and Hasbro states "This addition will be the jewel of your collection." Sindy wears a frilly pink and tulle ballgown and accessories include a pendant, tiara, long white gloves, and pearly white dress shoes displayed on a satin pillow.

Party Letters Sindy
#8046 • 1990 • $45

Sindy comes complete with mini-stationery, ink and ink stamp to send out party invitations!

She wears a "mother-of-pearl" body suit with removable matching skirt accented with a party balloon motif and has a large pink felt, heart-shaped pocket that stores her "Sindy" pencil! A cute fuzzy cropped party jacket with large pouf sleeves completes the ensemble. Accesories include: white pearl heart shaped earrings and matching necklace.

Beautiful Bows Sindy
#8076 • 1990 • $65

This is one of my all-time favorite Sindy dolls in my own collection. Sindy's hair and facial painting are flawless! Sindy wears a form-fitting pink and white striped satin gown with pink and purple nylon netting tulle underlays. Her large accent bows are removable so the little owner of the doll can place them in her own hair. The overall satin fabric is accented with mini-purple bow print. Gold bow designed earrings and choker are Sindy's choice for accessories. Her shoes are pink low heels with purple bow accents.

Edwardian Dream Sindy
#8163 • 1991 • $85

This entry is with no doubt Hasbro International's first attempt to gear to the collector market! The box is collector style and Hasbro even states with box graphics that Sindy is displayed in a special collector presentation pack and is a collector's dream come true.

Sindy looks the epitome of old-fashioned glamour in her classic gown of cream and ivory print with lace accents and cream satin accent and rosettes. Her matching parasol and feather trimmed hat are perfect finishing touches. Hasbro International displays Sindy's high-heeled strap pumps in an adorable doll size shoe box!

Pop Star Sindy
#8108 • 1991 • $55

Sindy's latest record has just hit the U.K.'s #1 position and Sindy's all smiles and ready to perform before a SRO crowd at the Palladium! Her stage costume consists of purple lamé body suit, removable ruffled skirt, yellow/lime fitted jacket with wild and wonderful matching streaked hair! Yellow boots complete her stage costume.

Beach Dazzle Sindy
#18251 • 1992 • $25

Sindy is ready for a day of volleyball and picnicking with her friends at the beach. She has that '60s look with long blonde flip hair style and bold abstract print helenca swimsuit and matching headband. Her earrings are large and look as though she forgot to remove them when she went to the ball with Paul the night before!

Sindy Go Go
#18276 • 1992 • $75

This terrific gift set really sent sales flying, especially for the Canadian market! Mattel/Toronto made a similar gift set for exclusive sale in the Canadian Zeller Store Chain of their popular Barbie doll with a walking pup. Their set was called "Barbie and Her Roll-along Pup" and can be seen on page 45. This colorful gift set has Sindy all decked out in a vibrant purple knit jumpsuit and colorful dog motif print satin baseball jacket. The adorable pet dog is battery operated and will start to work only when Sindy is holding the leash.

Options Collection
#18288 • 1992 • $24

Sindy sets out for a career as a doctor here. There are lots of included accessories such as a stethoscope, doctor bag, patient chart and ID badge.

Options Collection
#18288-02 • 1992 • $24

Sindy will take on the best of them! Watch out Julia Child! Sindy becomes a gourmet chef and her accessories include a gourmet frying skillet and all of the cooking utensils. This is a really cute set!

Mix and Match Collection
#18302 • 1992 • $24

Sindy's contemporary sportswear includes a black leather bomber jacket with silver piping, red denim jeans, white tank top and colorful print scarf. Her cool accessories include black ankle boots, red headband and black shades!

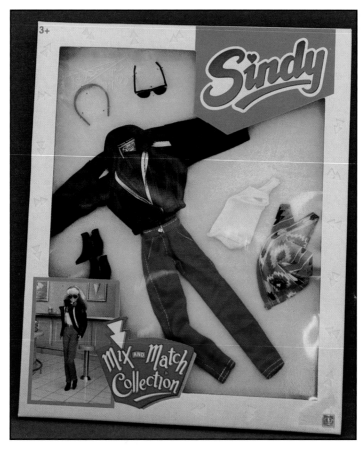

Romance 'N Roses Sindy
#18294 • 1992 • $85

This beauty was a top of the line entry for Hasbro International. Sindy gets all decked out in the season's finest ball gown for her big date with best beau Paul! Sindy chooses a taffeta rosebud print gown that is gathered below the waist and bodice. Nylon netting underskirts give the gown extra fullness and three satin roses are accented on the bustline. Simulated rhinestones are placed randomly on the large billowy sleeves and neckline and Sindy chooses pearl and silver drop earrings for accessories along with smart looking pink sling back pumps. Her flowing hair is highlighted with a barrette with smaller scale versions of the three bodice rosettes! This is truly a breathtaking doll for Hasbro International.

Romance Paul
#18295 • 1992 • $45

The lead Hasbro Sindy doll for 1993 was Romance 'N Roses. Sindy's best beau Paul was the matching counterpart to this concept. Paul looks dashing in his formal wear of double breasted raspberry satin jacket with black satin lapels. He completes the ensemble with black satin trousers with pink and silver metallic piping down the legs and white formal shirt and pink iridescent bow tie. He is prepared to pick Sindy up at her house for their big night out carrying a florist corsage with card attached, "To Sindy, Love Always, Paul."

Surprise Jeans Sindy
#18333 • 1993 • $45

Here is a great innovative play doll! Sindy has brunette long, silky straight hair with auburn highlights. Her "mod" clothing consists of a fluorescent orange and hot pink nylon geometric print T-shirt, purple vinyl bell bottom slacks, matching bandanna, and orange fringe suede shoulder bag. The surprise here is when the little owner washes the vinyl bell bottoms and bandanna they will uncover the three available bold patterned cotton bell bottom slacks! Note Sindy's whimsical chimpanzee dangle earrings too!

Monte Carlo Sindy
#18381 • 1993 • $30

This version of Sindy is really gorgeous for a moderately priced release. Her chestnut brown hair is beautifully rooted in a sidepart, soft-end curl flip. Her frilly hot pink and orange bikini show off the new Sindy modifications Hasbro did to her that year. Her abdomen is defined with the look of a real ribcage and Sindy even has a navel!

Fairy Princess Sindy
#18389 • 1993 • $55

Hasbro International delivers us a three in one play concept doll here. Sindy is dressed in a fairy princess gown of pink shimmering tulle and her locks have glittery woven strands throughout. The gown has removable pieces and can be transformed into a short ballerina type costume and reversed to a white pearl look that becomes a flying magical fairy when the child adds on the golden wings also included.

Wild Hair Sindy
#18385 • 1993 • $55

Another great play doll! Sindy has long brunette crimped hair with interwoven auburn highlights. She has two round holes concealed in her hair so that one can "pop" in one of four wild hairpieces to create numerous fashion looks! A child-size hair clip is included and the child can take these hair pieces and clip them into the child-size clip and wear that in their own hair! Sindy wears a yellow and gold Lycra minidress with a wild style black and white zebra print vest that ties in the front with a green and black satin ribbon accented with "love beads." Her accessories include a black and white striped hair bow, pink drop earrings, and lime green ankle boots.

Paradise Sindy
#18409 • 1994 • $30

Hasbro International and Sindy once again salute the late '60s with a retro-Sindy doll. Sindy looks like a "flower child" in her tie-dyed bold colored one piece swimsuit. She mirrors the typical '60s hair style — long, center-parted straight hair, with a "flower child" headband worn across the forehead. Her soft lavender eyes and striking magenta lipstick make this girl an eyecatcher!

SINDY

Party Lights
#041648 • 1992 • $55

Sindy will be the hit of the party with Hasbro's innovative play concept here. The doll has a battery operated mechanism in her back. When one moves her arm upwards, Sindy's fiber-optic hair changes, like a strobe light, to various colors of the rainbow. Sindy wears a cute multi-colored print party dress with ruffle accents. One of the coolest Sindy's to date!

"I Love Glitter Nails" Sindy
#18466 • 1994 • $45

This is rather a strange concept doll. The enclosed nail polish is intended for the child to use and not for use on the Sindy doll. Sindy is wearing a gold lamé cocktail dress with a glittery pink overcoat. Sindy lost her fashion know-how here with the choice of silver accent earrings, necklace and belt buckle! Guess she watched the animated holiday classic "Rudolph the Red Nose Reindeer" once too often and took Burle Ives rendition of the song "Silver and Gold" too seriously!

DOLL INDEX

Listed in alphabetical order by name.